G000278031

MARINE ENGINES
AND BOATING MECHANICS

MARINE ENGINES
AND BOATING MECHANICS

Dermot Wright

DAVID & CHARLES : NEWTON ABBOT

0 7153 5988 6

© Dermot Wright 1973

First published 1973
Second impression 1977
Third impression 1978

All rights reserved. No part of this publication
may be reproduced, stored in a retrieval system,
or transmitted, in any form or by any means,
electronic, mechanical, photocopying, recording or
otherwise, without the prior permission of
David & Charles (Publishers) Limited

Printed in Great Britain
by Redwood Burn Limited, Trowbridge & Esher
for David & Charles (Publishers) Limited
Brunel House Newton Abbot Devon

CONTENTS

Contents

LIST OF ILLUSTRATIONS

Diagrams
Fig   *Page*

The plates listed above are reproduced with the permission of the following: Brit Engineering (Manufacturing) Co Ltd for 23; W. H. Den Ouden N.V. Rotterdam for 19 and 20; Dorman Diesels Ltd, Kelvin Marine Division, for 31 and 33; Dowty Hydraulic Drive Units Ltd for 7; Enfield Industrial Engines Ltd for 9; Ford Motor Company Ltd for 28–30; G & M Power Plant Co Ltd for 11 and 12; G-Power Marine Ltd for 27; Hamble Foundry Ltd for 5 and 6; Honda (UK) Ltd for 3 and 4; Lister Blackstone Mirrlees Marine Ltd for 1 and 21; Lucas-CAV Marine for 13–18; Mercedes-Benz (Great Britain) Ltd for 26; Perkins Engine Group for 24; Powerco Ltd for 2; SAAB-SCANIA Automotive Products Group, Sweden for 10; A. B. Volvo Penta, Sweden for 8; Watermota Ltd for 22 and 25; and Yacht Chandlers of Great Britain Ltd for 32.

The diagrams are reproduced with permission as follows: Alkaline Batteries Ltd for Fig 7; Brit Engineering (Manufacturing) Co Ltd for Fig 2; Bryce Berger Ltd for Fig 8; Dowty Hydraulic Drive Ltd for Fig 13; English Electric Diesels Ltd, Kelvin Marine Division, for Figs 1, 3, 4, 9–12, 15, 17–23; Lucas-CAV Marine for Figs 5 and 6; Nicor Marine Ltd for Fig 16; and Watermota Ltd for Fig 14.

INTRODUCTION

During the last decade many changes have taken place in the design, materials and methods of manufacture of small craft. Changed too are the attitudes of the people who buy and use them. Today some form of auxiliary power is often considered essential for even quite small sailing craft and because of its permanence and simplicity an inboard engine is often the choice.

In sea-going yachts and power cruisers, fishing boats and workboats, the inboard engine is a natural part of the specification, and much attention has been paid to producing both true marine units and marinised conversions of suitable automobile engines.

While the modern, moderate-powered marine engine is reliable, simple to operate and economical, it nevertheless requires care, attention and understanding if it is to function instantly and effectively when required.

Every year more and more people take to the water in newly acquired boats, and while the rudiments of boat handling and navigation may be quickly acquired, knowledge of the internal combustion engine is often limited to lifting the bonnet of the car and having the garage mechanic top it up with oil and water.

Such is the reliability of the modern car engine that an owner can drive for thousands of miles each year without thinking about what may be going on in the engine compartment. If by chance the motor refuses to start, or stops when it should be going there is always the telephone to summon rapid assistance.

Introduction

It is a different matter in a boat. An unreliable, temperamental, difficult-to-start or—worse still—a hitherto reliable engine which unexpectedly fails to start or keep running, can put a ship and her crew in hazard, extraction from which may be no closer than the time required for a distress signal to be sent and acted upon.

Some understanding, then, of the marine power unit and its ancillary equipment is an important adjunct to good seamanship. This does not imply that the average boat owner needs to become a marine engineer. No more is essential than an appreciation of how the various units operate and what is required in the way of routine attention to keep them going. Failures due to serious mechanical effects, breakage of components or resulting from excessive or fair wear and tear will be beyond the scope of the majority of the non-technical. In such cases professional attention will be needed.

The purpose of this book is to explain in straightforward, non-technical language how the inboard engine works and to describe those of its component parts and auxiliary equipment in such a way that even the owner without mechanical inclinations can, if he wishes, acquire some knowledge of what goes on in the engine-room or under the floorboards.

Although there is a close inter-relationship between all the components of a yacht's power installation—engine, gearbox, stern gear, generators, batteries, and so on—the material is arranged in such a way that each section or chapter is complete within itself. The book may thus be read through as an informative work giving a broad picture of the whole subject, or it can be used for reference to specific items and their function.

The subject is restricted to inboard power units installed as an integral part of the yacht which the owner lives with when aboard and which, because it cannot be readily taken ashore for immediate professional attention, calls at times upon his own skill and resourcefulness.

AUTHOR'S NOTE

Wherever applicable throughout the book symbols and abbreviations are given in accordance with the recommendations of British Standard 1991: Part I: 1967. For example, 'rev/min' replaces the older rpm, 'in' replaces the inch sign ″ and 'ft' replaces the foot sign . Again, 'lbf' is used for pound-force, as in measurement of torque. Horsepower is 'hp', watt is 'W' and watt hour 'Wh', volt is 'V', ampere is 'A' and ampere hour 'Ah', 'Btu' is British thermal unit, and so on.

CHAPTER I

THE ENGINE

Although the internal combustion (IC) engine used in yachts, lifeboats, workboats and other small craft varies widely in configuration and power output, the operating principles do not change. Whether the engine is a single cylinder, multi cylinder, horizontally opposed, V form, four stroke or two stroke, petrol or diesel, it runs on a continually repeated cycle in which fuel is drawn in, compressed, ignited and discharged.

To maintain the cycle the engine must suck in considerable quantities of air, or air/fuel mixture, and this is achieved by fitting a piston tightly in a cylinder so that when it is moved up and down in the cylinder it acts as a pump.

Power is created by periodic ignition of fuel in the cylinder. The resulting rapid expansion of the burning gases imparts a considerable force to the piston, moving it down the cylinder and, by means of a connecting rod and crank, turning the crankshaft.

The IC engine is thus a heat machine using as its motivating force energy derived from burning a volatile fuel. There are two types of fuel—petrol and diesel oil. With either there are two types of engine—four stroke and two stroke. In the four stroke the valves, which control the entry and discharge of the fuel mixture and exhaust gases, are external components operating in the cylinder head. In the two-stroke unit the valves (called ports) are internal, being formed as openings in the cylinder walls which are covered and uncovered by piston movement.

While the two-stroke engine is little used in road vehicles

(other than the motorcycle) it is very much in evidence in marine units, both petrol and diesel. Basically the difference between the two configurations lies in the number of power strokes per complete cycle. In the two stroke this is every second stroke, in the four stroke it is every fourth stroke.

In the petrol engine the fuel has to be mixed with air to form a combustible gas before it enters the engine. In order that it shall mix properly it must be atomised—that is broken up into fine particles. This is achieved in the carburettor which meters fuel through a small jet located within and at right angles to an air stream moving in the induction tube, in which there is variable restriction known as the throttle. As the throttle is opened more air flows through, more petrol is drawn from the jet and more fuel mixture enters the engine which consequently runs faster and gives increased power.

The combustible mixture is attained differently in the diesel engine, although in either type the system of valves—two stroke or four stroke—is the same. Here air is drawn in separately and highly compressed which causes it to become very hot. At the right moment a metered quantity of diesel oil fuel is squirted into it under pressure. The fuel vaporises and the mixture immediately ignites—hence the term compression ignition—no electrical ignition being required. Electrical ignition is required in the petrol engine to ignite the compressed fuel mixture. This is achieved by the sparking plug in which a high voltage electric current is made to jump a gap between two electrodes (points). The resulting spark, which occurs at precisely the right moment on the compression stroke, ignites the fuel mixture.

The opening and closing of the valves and the production of a spark in the petrol engine, or an injection of fuel in the diesel, are arranged mechanically through drive mechanisms operated by the camshaft which is driven at half engine speed by the crankshaft. Accurate valve and ignition timing are an essential part of the cyclic operation of the engine.

On ignition the fuel mixture must burn—not explode— rapidly and evenly over the piston crown and in achieving this the degree to which the fuel mixture is compressed is a characteristic of design which also determines, in a petrol engine particularly, the grade of fuel which should be used. In modern petrol engines the compression ratio is around 8 or 9 to 1, that is, the fuel mixture is compressed to an eighth or ninth of its original volume. In the diesel unit the ratio is much higher, 22 to 1 being

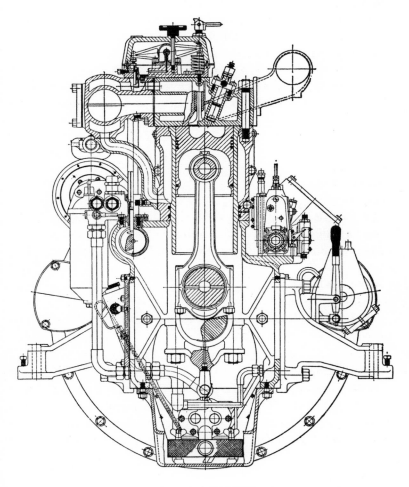

Fig 1   Cross-section layout of a marine diesel engine

quite common, because of the necessity of raising the temperature of the air to, or above, the flash-point temperature of the diesel fuel.

Compression must be maintained if an engine is to give its designed performance and this calls for structural strength and leak proof combustion chambers, valves and pistons. Because of the much higher compression ratio the diesel unit has to be a great deal stronger than the petrol engine and so is heavier and the initial cost is higher. Diesels, however, burn the fuel more efficiently and are less costly to run.

The basic operations—fuel mixture, compression, ignition and exhausting burnt mixture—are achieved by a cycle of operations which is the same for both the petrol and diesel four-stroke and two-stroke engines.

PETROL (four stroke)

Induction stroke

Piston going down.

Inlet valve open, exhaust valve closed. The descending piston causes a reduction of pressure in the cylinder which induces fuel mixture to flow in from the inlet manifold through the inlet valve.

Compression stroke

Piston ascending.

Inlet and exhaust valves closed. Fuel mixture being compressed in the combustion chamber.

Power stroke

Both valves closed. Spark plug spark ignites compressed fuel mixture which rapidly expands, forcing piston down on the 'working' stroke of the cycle. The force working on the piston is transmitted through the connecting rod to the crankshaft.

Exhaust stroke

Exhaust valve open, piston rising. Inlet valve closed. Burnt gases forced out via exhaust valve. At the end of this stroke the inlet valve opens and the cycle starts again.

The working stroke gives the power to turn the engine. During the other strokes the machine is in effect idling. So a flywheel is needed to maintain the inertia of the power stroke and keep the engine turning until the next power stroke. Without a flywheel it would be virtually impossible to start or run an IC engine, whether it be single or multi cylinder.

The single-cylinder four-stroke engine, having only one power stroke in four, is relatively rough running and is only nowadays found in the smallest marine units. Next in size comes the twin-cylinder unit with two power strokes for every two revolutions of the crankshaft, the firing of the fuel mixture being arranged so that power strokes occur in each cylinder alternatively, thus introducing a balancing element.

In the multi-cylinder engine firing takes place in a sequence designed to achieve the smoothest possible operation and keep

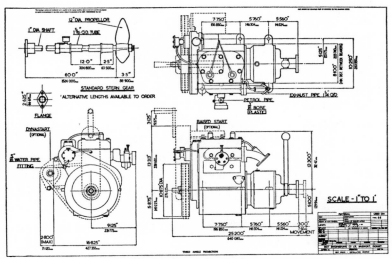

Fig 2   BRIT petrol engine and stern gear detail

stresses to a minimum. In a four-cylinder unit, for example, the firing order is usually 1,2,4,3 or 1,3,4,2 the cylinders being numbered from the front to the rear of the engine.

The same cycle of operations takes place in the diesel engine but, as previously explained, the method of igniting the fuel mixture is different. The operations are:

DIESEL (four stroke)

Induction stroke

Piston going down.

Inlet valve open, exhaust valve closed. The descending piston causes a reduction of pressure in the cylinder which induces air to flow in through the inlet valve.

Compression stroke

Piston ascending.

Inlet and exhaust valves closed. Air being compressed into combustion chamber area.

Just before maximum compression is attained diesel fuel is squirted in through an injector nozzle. Because of the heat it immediately vapourises, mixes with the air and ignites.

Power stroke

Both valves closed.

Piston descends activated by the pressure of the rapidly expanding burning fuel/air mixture. This is the 'working' stroke of the cycle in which the force working on the piston is transmitted through the connecting rod to the crankshaft.

Exhaust stroke

Exhaust valve open, piston rising. Inlet valve closed. Burnt gases forced out via exhaust valve.

At the end of this stroke the inlet valve opens and the cycle starts again.

In the theoretical consideration of the four-stroke cyclic operation valve opening and closing is related to the piston at top or bottom dead centre (TDC or BDC). In practice this would not be possible because there is a small time lag between initial ignition and complete burning of the fuel mixture, or charge, in the cylinder. Valve timing is therefore arranged to provide valve overlap by which both inlet and exhaust valves are at times open together. Overlap allows the exhaust valve to open just before the piston reaches BDC on the power stroke and to close just after TDC on the exhaust stroke. The inlet valve opens a

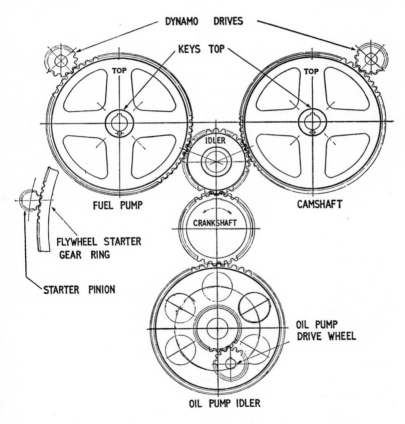

Fig 3   Typical timing gear arrangement

little before TDC on the exhaust stroke and closes slightly after BDC on the induction stroke. The result is maximum filling of the cylinder with incoming charge and quickest and most complete discharge of exhaust gases.

The same principle applies in the ignition timing, the spark (or injection of diesel fuel) being arranged to occur somewhat before TDC on the compression stroke.

The two-stroke engine operates on a different principle, having no external valves and using the crankcase as a partial compression chamber. In the petrol version petrol is mixed with air in a carburettor before being fed into the engine, in the same way as for the four stroke. In the diesel two stroke, air only is drawn in and compressed before the diesel fuel is squirted in.

The operation cycle differs from the four stroke in that there is a power stroke for only one revolution of the crankshaft. The valve system consists of an inlet and exhaust ports located in the side of the cylinder and a transfer port connecting the crankcase with the cylinder. As the piston moves up and down in the cylinder it covers and uncovers these ports and allows fuel mixture or air in and exhaust gases out. The operational sequence is:

PETROL AND DIESEL (two stroke)

Induction stroke

Piston descends. As the piston goes down it uncovers the exhaust port and increases pressure in the crankcase into which fuel mixture (or air) has been introduced by the previous compression stroke in which the piston uncovered the inlet port. Exhaust gases are forced out through the exhaust port and fuel mixture (or air) is forced from the crankcase to the cylinder through the transfer port.

Compression stroke

Piston rises, compressing the fuel mixture (or air) covering the transfer port and uncovering the inlet port.

Power stroke

At maximum compression the spark occurs (or diesel oil is injected) and the mixture ignites, forcing the piston down and imparting, through the connecting rod and crank, torque to the crankshaft.

Exhaust stroke

As the piston descends on the power stroke it uncovers the exhaust port, covers the inlet port, and finally uncovers the transfer port.

The sequence then starts again.

Common to all types of IC engine, petrol and diesel, four stroke and two stroke, is the need for efficient cooling without which the machinery would rapidly become too hot to function. Two types of cooling media are employed—air and water. In either case a means must be provided of cooling the coolant. In the air-cooled unit this is done by providing a constant flow of air past the engine—usually by ducting and an engine-driven fan, or, with very small single-cylinder engines, mounting in a well-ventilated area in the boat.

However, the majority of marine engines are water cooled, either by raw water taken direct from the sea, river or lake, or by a closed circuit fresh-water system in which the cooling water is itself cooled by raw water through a heat exchanger. Water circulation, by mechanical engine-driven pumps is through water jackets surrounding the cylinders and often other components such as the sump and exhaust system.

Equally important is lubrication. The IC marine engine, like any other piece of machinery having moving parts which rub together, metal to metal, requires the provision of a film of oil constantly maintained between such parts. Without such lubrication an engine could only run for a short while before severe overheating caused bearings to run and pistons to seize in the cylinders.

Cooling and lubrication, as well as other aspects of the IC

marine engine, will be given more detailed treatment later. In this first chapter basic operating principles have been described. If these are understood, engine management by even the non-technically minded is made easier. Modern marine engines are not the temperamental beast of earlier years. Nevertheless a systematic approach to engine handling, particularly in regard to starting techniques, is well worthwhile. And here may be given a titbit of advice which is so often ignored. Follow the manufacturer's instructions. Strange though it may seem he knows his product better than anyone else and the operating and maintenance procedures given in the engine handbook result from knowledge and experience which the private owner is seldom in a position to acquire.

CHAPTER 2

COMPONENT PARTS

PISTONS

Of all the internal parts of the marine engine the piston probably has the most arduous duties. It has to withstand the pressure and heat of the burning fuel and transmit the resulting energy to the connecting rod. It must not allow burning or burnt gases to escape past it and it must keep the cylinder walls free from excess oil. Because its motion is reciprocating, it stops and changes direction at each end of every stroke, many hundreds of times per minute.

A piston must therefore be strong, but light in weight and free from excessive expansion when heated. The material from which it is made has to be carefully chosen and today it is invariably an aluminium alloy which is lighter and conducts heat away quicker than cast iron which used to be employed.

However, when heated, aluminium alloy expands more than cast iron and so considerable design skill is necessary to accommodate the resulting change in dimensions. Several methods are used. In the split-skirt system slots are cut at various angles in the portion of the piston below the rings. Or pistons are ground elliptical rather than truly circular so that they take a circular shape when heated.

PISTON RINGS

Because of the expansion factor pistons cannot be fitted tightly in the cylinders or they would seize up when hot. Therefore some clearance is given and piston rings are used to maintain compression. These are usually made of highly resilient cast iron and located in grooves cut in the upper part of the piston. The upper two, or sometimes three, are the compression rings and the lower one the scraper ring.

In action the compression rings are forced downwards and outwards by the expanding gases so that they impinge tightly against the cylinder walls and prevent loss of compression. The scraper ring removes the excess of oil which would otherwise accumulate on the cylinder walls.

GUDGEON PINS

The piston is attached to the little end of the connecting rod by a short spindle known as the gudgeon pin. Made from high tensile steel forging or specially forged aluminium alloy such as Duralumin or Hiduminium, gudgeon pins are either fitted tightly in the little end by pressing or clamping, or they are of the fully floating type which have freedom of movement in both the little end and the piston, in which case they are kept in position by circlips.

CONNECTING RODS

The connecting rod is again a high tensile steel forging. At its lower end it contains the big end bearing which forms the connection between the rod and the crankpin of the crankshaft. The big end is split to enable it to be assembled with the bearing, on the crankpin, by bringing the two halves together and clamping up with high tensile steel bolts.

CRANKSHAFT

The crankshaft may be a high tensile steel forging or special high grade cast iron. It has a crankpin for each cylinder, journals on which it turns in the main bearings, and webs, or cranks, which act as balance weights and connect the pins and journals.

One end of the crankshaft carries an attachment for the flywheel, while the camshaft drive is usually taken from the other end. Drilled oilways running from the journals to the crankpins allow for pressure lubrication to big end and main bearings.

BEARINGS

Even when the engine is operating at normal cruising rev/min all these components are moving at considerable speeds and to prevent overheating and rapid failure special little end, big end and crankshaft bearings are required. These are of white metal, a special alloy which, although relatively soft, has high-wear resistance, low friction and low melting point, so that should overheating occur, as could happen with oil pressure failure, for example, partial 'running' or fusing of this metal would safeguard against destructive total seizure. No machining is necessary when fitting these bearings. They are supplied as standard parts for slipping in to the bearing housings.

CYLINDER BLOCK AND CRANKCASE

The main external components of the engine are the cylinder block and crankcase. These are castings, usually of cast iron, but sometimes of light alloys. In the block are machined the cylinder bores in which the pistons operate either in direct surface contact with the metal of the block, or within special cast iron or steel cylindrical liners. Machined passages and holes in the block provide for coolant circulation, valve-operating components and the attachment of various items such as water pump, distributor and fuel pump.

The crankcase provides housing for the main crankshaft bearings, and the camshaft bearings and thrust bearings. It also provides location and means of attachment for the sump, the dished component at the lowest part of the engine which holds the reservoir of lubricating oil.

Component Parts

CYLINDER HEAD

On top of the block is fitted the cylinder head, a machined detachable unit of cast iron or aluminium, containing inlet and exhaust ports, valves and, in the petrol engine, sparking plugs. Past practice has been to locate the combustion chamber—in which the fuel is compressed and fired—in the cylinder head, but today some cylinder heads are flat, the combustion chamber being recessed into the head of the piston.

Other functions of the cylinder head are to house the valve guides and valve seats and provide attachment points for the inlet and exhaust manifolds and the valve rocker shaft which carries the valve rocker mechanism.

VALVES AND VALVE GEAR

The flow of gases—fuel in, exhaust out—is controlled by the valves. Machined from special heat-resisting materials, these have ground faces on the underside of the heads so that they make a gas-tight joint with the valve seats. They are held in the closed position by the valve springs and forced open, against the pressure of the springs, by a push exerted on the stem by the rocker arm. The rocker arms pivot on the rocker shaft, being activated by push rods which, through cam followers or tappets, are lifted by cams on the camshaft.

In this mechanical linkage between cam and valve it is necessary to have a small gap somewhere so that the valve can seat fully without restriction when closed. This gap is known as the tappet clearance and is usually set or adjusted between the valve stem and the rocker arm.

CAMSHAFT

In a push-rod four-stroke engine the camshaft is located inside the crankcase in such a position that the push rods are parallel to the pistons It is driven from the crankshaft by sprocket wheels and chain, or gears, at half engine speed.

Component Parts

Alternatively one or two camshafts can be positioned above the cylinder head, in which case the unit is known as an overhead camshaft engine (OHC), either single or twin. Drive is by sprockets and chain or, with increasing frequency today, toothed pulleys and matching toothed rubber belt.

In the OHC arrangement push rods are eliminated and the cams actuate the valves direct through bucket tappets, tappet clearance being controlled by the insertion of shims, or by single rocker arms in which case the gap is set in the same way as in the push rod unit.

The way the cams are set on the camshaft in relation to the position of the pistons on their various strokes, and the actual cam profiles, have a fundamental bearing on the behaviour, power output and fuel consumption of the engine.

CYLINDER LAYOUTS

The arrangement of the cylinders in relation to the crankshaft in a maritime engine depends on a number of design factors, one of which, in the faster-running units, is the need to limit crankshaft length. Three basic configurations are used: vertical in line, in which the cylinders are arranged one behind the other (looking from front to rear of the engine) vertically above the crankshaft; horizontally opposed, in which the cylinders lie horizontally opposite each other with the crankshaft between them; or in V formation in which the cylinders are placed above the crankshaft in two lines, or banks, at an angle to each other forming a V varying from 60° to 90°.

Six-cylinder vertical in line and V eight layouts are most frequently used in higher-powered engines, being well balanced mechanically, smooth in torque output and having relatively short crankshafts, a desirable factor because longer crankshafts tend to whip and so need more main bearings.

In the medium horse power range the four-cylinder in line layout is almost universally used, although horizontally opposed fours are also produced which smooth the running because both mechanical movements and firing strokes are equally balanced.

For small boats there are single- and twin-cylinder engines ranging in power output from about 1½hp upwards. For many years engines in this range were petrol two strokes of the petrol/oil type, lubrication being obtained by mixing a small amount of lubricating oil with the petrol. More recently the development and increased popularity of the small auxiliary sailing boats and family and fishing cruisers has led to a demand for diesel engines in the lower-power ranges and this has been met by the production of a number of single- and twin-cylinder units.

Page 33: 1 (*above*) Lister HA 3MA engine with Lyons 17½kW alternator; 2 (*below*) Powerco 30kW 110-60V dc charging set powered by Perkins 4·236 engine

Page 34: 3 (*above*) Honda ED250 6V 9A, 12V 14.5A, 24V 9A, 250W dc generator; 4 (*below*) Honda EC1500 220V, ac, 50 cycles, 1kW generator

CHAPTER 3

FUEL SUPPLY

In the petrol engine a process of carburation, that is charging air with finely divided particles of hydrocarbon fuel, is used to produce a combustible mixture which will burn rapidly, evenly and cleanly.

While the main component is the carburettor, the inlet manifold, inlet valves, combustion chamber and pistons all play their part in producing this fuel mixture and delivering it to the cylinders at the right time.

The sequence starts when petrol, fed to the carburettor from the supply tank by gravity or pump, is first mixed with air. The carburettor has two main parts, the float chamber in which a reservoir of petrol is maintained by a float-actuated needle valve and the venturi, a circular air passage having a restriction, or 'waist'.

The principle of operation is as follows: petrol from the float chamber is carried by pipe to the main jet which is situated in the venturi at right angles to the airstream. Air is induced to flow through the carburettor by the partial vacuum created by the pistons when the engine is turning. As the air passes through the venturi its speed is increased and pressure reduced. The pressure reduction creates a suction in the jet and petrol is drawn into the airstream and vapourised. The petrol/air mixture is then carried along through the inlet manifold, past the inlet valve and into the relevant cylinder where it is compressed and ignited on the firing stroke.

The rate of flow and quantity of air passing through the

carburettor is controlled by the throttle, a variable valve set in the venturi tube which may be·set in any position from closed to open by means of the throttle lever. In marine installations the throttle lever is often linked in a single control with the gear-selection mechanism. As the throttle is opened the air flow through the venturi speeds up, more petrol is drawn from the jet and the engine runs faster and gives more power.

The petrol must remain vapourised—and thus properly mixed with the air—during the whole of its passage from the venturi to the combustion chamber. Any local cooling of the passages, such as could occur in certain places in the inlet manifold, could convert the petrol back to droplets. It is for this reason that inlet manifolds are often separately heated.

The carburettor has other duties and is consequently somewhat more sophisticated than the above description implies. Unlike automotive engines a marine engine is required to run for long periods at relatively low cruising rev/min and it must do this economically using as little fuel as possible. This requires a relatively low ratio of petrol to air, probably in the region of 15 parts of air to 1 part of petrol measured by weight. Alternatively a somewhat richer mixture is required for full throttle, maximum power operation, and a very rich mixture is needed to start a petrol engine from cold, say about 3:1 or even 1:1.

Carburettors fall into two main types: fixed jet and variable jet. The essential difference between the two lies in the method used to induce petrol into the air flow and deal with the need to progressively reduce the petrol content as the air flow speeds up, because, although air reduces in density as it flows faster, petrol does not and so without some form of automatic compensation the mixture would become progressively too rich as the throttle was opened.

In the fixed-jet carburettor this problem is dealt with by mixing some air with petrol before it is drawn into the venturi. There are two ways of doing this, some carburettors having an emulsion tube, others a compensating jet. Many fixed-jet carburettors incorporate an accelerator pump which supplies the extra petrol needed when the engine is rapidly accelerated.

Fuel Supply

In the variable-jet carburettor the area of the venturi throat is variable by means of a sliding piston to which is attached a tapered needle valve operating in the main jet to regulate the supply of petrol. The principle of operation is simple. As the throttle is opened the piston rises, enlarging the venturi area and withdrawing the tapered needle from the fuel supply tube (jet), thus increasing the flow of fuel mixture to the engine. As the throttle is closed the piston descends, partially blocking the venturi area and, by lowering the tapered needle valve, limiting the flow of fuel. The specially rich cold starting mixture is provided by a mechanical linkage which lowers the jet in relation to the tapered needle.

There are a number of different makes of both types of carburettor, each incorporating individual manufacturers' approach to the design and operational requirements. The fixed-jet unit has very few moving parts, all the required functions being achieved by fixed jets and fuel passages and fixed venturi areas. In the variable-jet version the requirements are met by the moving piston and needle valve. In each type the design and mechanical operation is such that adjustment and maintenance have been reduced to a minimum.

In the diesel engine the carburettor and inlet manifold are eliminated, diesel oil being injected into each cylinder by means of an engine-driven fuel injector pump via injector nozzles permanently located in the cylinder head.

The duty of the pump is to deliver a measured amount of diesel oil under pressure to each cylinder nozzle at the precise moment on the compression stroke when the air is at its highest temperature. Although simple enough in principle of operation and in engineering and construction, diesel pumps are precise pieces of equipment requiring delicate adjustment. The pump plungers, one for each cylinder injection nozzle, are activated by cams on a camshaft driven by the engine. Fuel is fed from the main supply tank under pressure and phased to the cylinders at predetermined intervals. The amount of fuel delivered to the cylinders is variable according to whether the engine is required

37

to idle, run at cruising rev/min or give full power. The control mechanism for this variable metering is connected direct to the lever known generally, but not strictly correctly in the case of a diesel engine, as the throttle lever. This, as in the petrol engine, is often combined jointly with the gear-selection lever to give the operator a single control.

The injector nozzle is also a delicate piece of mechanism requiring fine adjustment. Actuated by pressure overcoming a spring-loaded valve, it must release exactly the right amount of fuel at precisely the right moment of the compression stroke and ensure that the fuel is properly atomised and thoroughly mixed with the air so that it obtains the oxygen necessary for correct burning.

These requirements are determined to a great extent by the design and shape of the combustion chamber which is often of a more complicated nature than is the case with the petrol engine. And for this reason there are many different kinds of injector nozzles. It is important that the nozzle should be kept in good condition so that the spray pattern remains correct, enabling the engine to function properly at all speeds.

The direct fuel-injection system can also be used on petrol engines, but because the cost is high and the servicing requires expert knowledge, this system is usually found only in high-performance and racing power units.

Again, as in the diesel, petrol injection eliminates the carburettor and inlet manifold. Metered quantities of petrol are forced into the cylinders by pressure-fed injector nozzles located in the inlet passages near the inlet valves. Operation of the system is either mechanical, by a metering distributor, or electronic, by solenoids with computer control. Both systems require petrol to be fed under pressure from the main tank and this is done by an electrically driven pump. The main advantages of the petrol-injection system are the high degree of control of the petrol/air mixture which can be precisely related to the engine-operating speeds and loads and the elimination of relatively inefficient components like the carburettor and inlet manifold. Petrol-injection engines show improved maximum power and acceleration—response to throttle openings being much more rapid—and reduction in fuel consumption.

In the more sophisticated, larger horse power installations it is seldom possible to rely on gravity for the petrol or diesel oil fuel feed to the engine, and a pump is installed to maintain a constant supply from the fuel storage tank. Pumps divide into two main types, mechanical and electric.

The mechanical pump, driven by the engine itself, has a rocker arm actuated by a cam which motivates a diaphragm against the pressure of a spring. The petrol flow is controlled by spring-loaded valves which prevent the fuel flowing to the carburettor when the float chamber is full, but at the same time allow the pump to operate. The top portion of the main chamber contains a filter and a sediment bowl and the mechanical pump can usually be identified by a characteristic transparent dome on the top.

The electric pump also uses a diaphragm to create the fuel flow but the operation is by solenoid instead of camshaft. A pair of contact points enables the solenoid to be energised and through mechanical linkage it pulls the diaphragm against the pressure of its spring. This draws fuel into the pump, the contacts then separate and the spring returns the diaphragm, pumping fuel to the engine. Electric fuel pumps do not have to be located close to the engine necessarily and so are not affected by engine heat. Also they operate as soon as the ignition or electric circuit is switched on.

Carburettor engines are often fitted with air cleaners which are used to prevent particles of dust and dirt blocking jets and entering the engine, causing wear in the cylinders and pistons. They also act as silencers, reducing the hiss of air entering the carburettor air intake. Where fitted an air silencer is designed as part of the fuel-breathing system of the engine. Construction is normally of metal, although plastic is now coming in automotive engineering. The filter element is usually paper, in concertina form, to give greater surface area, and which may be changed when necessary, or sometimes an oil bath and filter is employed.

In considering engine fuelling mention should be made of turbocharging as this system is frequently employed in diesel units in the larger horse power ranges, but is also being used in smaller engines, notably the four-cylinder Perkins T4.108M 1·76l four-stroke engine developing 65 shaft horse power.

Like a supercharger, the turbocharger's purpose is to uprate the specific power output of an existing engine by increasing the density of air intake into the cylinders. But, unlike the supercharger which is driven mechanically by the engine and thus absorbs some of the engine's power, the turbocharger is a compressor directly shaft coupled to a turbine driven by the flow of engine exhaust gases. By turbocharging much larger quantities of air may be forced into the engine cylinders than is possible by normal aspiration. This raises the engine's volumetric efficiency and more fuel can be fed to the extra air and so greater power output is obtained.

However, air entering an engine from a turbocharger is not only compressed, but at a higher temperature than atmospheric air and so its density is lowered. As increased efficiency depends upon the weight of air that can be got into the cylinders, it is necessary to cool the compressed air and so an intercooler— consisting of a number of tubes through which water is circulated —is introduced between the turbocharger's air outlet and the engine's air intake to cool the compressed air.

CHAPTER 4

TURBOCHARGING

Turbocharging, normally with intercooling, is a means of increasing the power output of an engine without adding very much extra weight and incurring a prohibitive increase in cost. It is essentially related to relatively high-speed engines such as are used in fast planing cruisers and, of course, racing boats, but turbocharged engines are also suitable for slower craft in which the high output obtained is harnessed by suitable reduction gearing and propeller design.

Basically turbocharging provides a means of increasing the breathing capacity of the engine. In a diesel (in which type of marine power unit turbocharging is usually employed) this means getting more air into the cylinders than would be possible by means of the engine's normal breathing. Assuming the combustion chamber remains the same in area, there is on the compression strokes a greater amount of air to be compressed and consequently it becomes much hotter. Then, when the fuel is injected the resulting ignition is more rapid and at higher temperature so that an appreciable increase in power results.

The greater the amount of air that can be got into the cylinders the higher, within reason, will be the power output of the engine. So intercooling is often used with turbocharging because by this means the air being forced into the cylinders is made cooler than it would otherwise be and at the lower temperature the density is greater, and thus more of it can be forced into the engine on the induction strokes.

A parallel to the engine's need for more air (or more fuel/air mixture in a petrol engine) can be seen in a human athlete running a race. At the start he is breathing (let us say) normally, the amount of air entering his lungs being sufficient to provide his system with the amount of oxygen needed for hopping about on the starting-line and perhaps some degree of nervous tension. As the race gets under way he starts to burn up energy and at the same time calls upon his system to provided more power. To respond, his system demands more fuel—primarily oxygen. To get more oxygen he must breathe harder and faster. Perhaps at a later stage, if the race is well within his capacity, he reaches a state of relative equilibrium. His breathing is regular and of sufficient depth to provide enough oxygen to keep him going at a steady pace. He is at cruising revs, in fact, and if we conveniently ignore factors such as muscular tiredness and the eventual need for food and drink—say fair wear and tear and fuel in the case of an engine—he might well go on like this for a considerable time.

But what happens if the race is highly competitive so that to win he must exert every ounce of physical and mental energy he can muster? He starts breathing much harder, taking in more and more air and forcing his system to greater effort, using his brain to co-ordinate all the working parts and keep abreast of competitors' tactics. To cope with all this physical and mental exertion he must get a greater amount of air into his lungs to increase the blood's oxygen supply. So again his breathing rate speeds up and his running rate becomes much faster. But this causes him to get very hot and lose a lot of body fluid and another demand is made on his air supply.

If when he reaches this stage a competitor is still outrunning him, he must make even more calls on his system. But there comes a point when he can no longer get more air into his lungs and even if he could, his main pump, the heart, is incapable of circulating the blood fast enough to supply the excessive demands for oxygen from muscle and brain. If he is not then near collapse, he is at least running at his maximum capacity.

And so it is with the normally aspirated engine. There comes a point when it can no longer be made to run faster. The speed of operation is such that the pistons, even at the high speed of their movement, can no longer induce more air into the cylinders and maximum speed has been reached.

At this point the parallel between engine and runner ceases because the engine designer has a remedy. He can provide the engine with a greater amount of air (or fuel/air mixture—for simplicity only the diesel engine will be referred to in this chapter; in so far as breathing and amount of fuel mixture is concerned, the principles are the same for petrol engines).

So much for the theory. What does turbocharging mean in practice? This can best be seen by looking in detail at the arrangement applied to a well-known marinised industrial engine, the basic Ford 89bhp Thames Trader truck engine which first came into being in 1960 and a version of which is today the highly successful 250bhp Turbo-Plus. To achieve such an increase in power demand special design skills in addition to the actual mechanical involvements of turbocharging and intercooling, because of the various effects on an engine of greatly increasing its power output.

But first let us analyse the mechanics of the two, related, systems. Turbocharging is in effect similar in principle to the once widely used supercharging. But it is different and mechanically superior. A supercharger increases the volume of air going into the engine by putting it under pressure and increasing the rate of flow through the induction system, as does the turbocharger. But in doing so it also takes some of the power increase back, for it has to be belt driven by the engine and so puts an additional mechanical loading on it.

A turbocharger, on the other hand, is a compressor shaft—coupled direct to a turbine driven by the engine exhaust gases. The rate of flow and heat of these gases is such that they contain considerable energy which in a normally aspirated engine goes to waste. As there is no mechanical linkage between the engine and the turbocharger, no engine power is absorbed in driving it. In fact, something is obtained for nothing.

Turbocharging

Although turbocharging increases the pressure of incoming air, which is an advantage, it also entails a disadvantage in that when air is compressed it heats up. An example is the bicycle pump which gets hot as air is forced into the tyre. As the temperature of air rises its density falls and so, paradoxically, the harder the turbocharger compresses the air, the more it heats it and the less is the amount that can be forced into the engine. To make this clear it is necessary to appreciate that higher power output

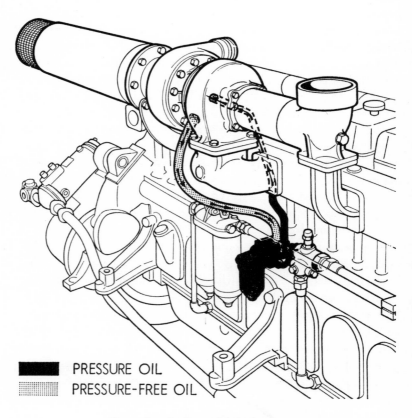

PRESSURE OIL
PRESSURE-FREE OIL

Fig 4   A turbocharger lubrication system

results from increasing the weight, rather than the volume, of air going into the cylinders.

Complementary to the turbocharger is the intercooler, a tubular device placed between the turbocharger's air outlet and the engine's air intake. The tubes are cooled by passing water through them—sea water is often used in a marine installation—and they in turn cool the high temperature air leaving the turbocharger. By the time this air reaches the engine most of the heat has been removed from it and, in consequence, its density has been raised. The increase in weight of the air can raise the efficiency of the engine by as much as 20 per cent over the turbocharged unit without an intercooler.

There is another gain. The working temperature of the engine is also kept down by the cooled air and so thermal stresses are reduced, particularly in the case of valves and valve seats, which has a beneficial effect on engine life.

These substantial gains in engine power output do not involve similarly substantial cost and weight penalties. There are, however, problems for the designer because any worthwhile increase in power output brings with it the need for design decisions affecting such matters as engine-operating speeds, the use of standard components, material specifications and operating temperatures. The Ford Turbo-Plus development affords one good example of how such problems were tackled by one particular design team.

As already mentioned the basic unit was the 89bhp truck engine, a normally aspirated six-cylinder 363in^3 diesel. This engine was selected for Ford's first application of turbocharging when uprated to 120bhp for industrial and marine use. Further experimental work in turbocharging was undertaken in 1965 and this resulted in the introduction in 1968 of the 150bhp vehicle engine, claimed to be Britain's first series production automotive turbocharged diesel. Industrial versions of this unit were soon available and a further power increase to 180bhp was achieved and introduced to the nautical world at the 1969 London International Boat Show.

This is where the story really begins, because the 180bhp engine was an immediate success, being widely used for marine applications, particularly by the racing people.

At this point it should perhaps be explained that Ford of Britain do not themselves turn out marine engines. It is their industrial engines that are used, these being marinised by outside specialist firms on Ford's approval. There is, of course, nothing detrimental in such an arrangement which is necessary because the number of marine engines required is only a small part of the substantial output of industrial engines coming from the factory in a year. If the manufacturer were to set up a marine division the relative costs would be out of proportion to the prices that could be charged for the marine units. A very close liaison is of course maintained between the Ford technicians and the approved marinising organisations. The boat owner gets the best of both worlds—a thoroughly reliable basic power unit backed by the solid experience of heavy duty industrial use, and the skills and knowledge of the specialist marine engineer.

However, to return to the development of the Turbo-Plus. The 180bhp engine—designated Turbo 360 2704ETI—proved reliable, particularly in racing, which showed that the design concept and materials specification were fundamentally right. It is not all that difficult to make an engine give a lot of power for a short time, but much more of a problem to achieve a substantial power increase with consistent reliability and long life. There were soon demands for even higher power and Ford, in conjunction with Simms Group Research and Developments Ltd, undertook to draw up an engine specification which would permit a continuous output of 250bhp to be safely achieved—70bhp more than the continuous rating of the 1969 engine—while keeping costs moderate and ensuring a high degree of reliability. Work began in May 1970 and by the end of the year sea trials were completed. The redeveloped engine gave all that was expected of it and, on the test bed, even higher power outputs.

It was not done without problems and self-imposed design

46

disciplines. The peak cylinder pressure, for example, was deliberately restricted to that of the 1969 engine, 1,800lb/in^2, and the proviso made that as far as possible the standard cylinder block, cylinder head, cylinder liners, crankshaft, connecting rods, valves and valve gear were to be retained. The desire to retain standard components was related to costs, of course, the intention being to eventually make the new engine available for general use and not solely as an expensive high-power racing unit. In fact many other standard items were retained such as the piston-ring pack consisting of three compression rings and one oil-control ring. The pistons, however, were redesigned to provide larger combustion cavities in the crowns. Standard fuel and lubricating oil filters were retained, as was the flywheel and crankshaft vibration damper.

In raising the power output of an existing engine the designer has the choice of two main alternatives. He can either increase the maximum crankshaft speed or raise the brake mean effective pressure (BMEP).

Increasing crankshaft speed means running all the engine's moving parts faster and the greater power is obtained at the expense of more noise, more vibration, faster wear and higher fuel consumption, all acceptable perhaps in a power unit intended solely for racing. But for general use, and the intention was that the developed engines should be suitable for high speed, luxury class cruising craft as well as racing machines, these penalties were considered too great and so the alternative approach was chosen.

Raising the BMEP, however, has the effect of increasing the peak cylinder pressure and this was not permissible above the limit of 1,800lb/in^2. The problem can be overcome by reducing the compression ratio and this was lowered to 13·7:1 which compares with 14·7:1 in the 180bhp engine and, as a matter of interest, 16·5:1 in the normally aspirated industrial six-cylinder diesel.

By lowering the compression ratio a BMEP of 223lb/in^2 was achieved, but the peak pressure has a maximum value of only 1,750lb/in^2, well within the design limitation. There was also a change in the fuel-injection characteristic to restrict peak pressure. The lowered compression ratio was obtained by increasing the volume of the combustion chamber through redesign of the pistons.

In a diesel engine low compression rates can cause cold start difficulties because a relatively high degree of compression is necessary to make the induced air hot enough to quickly ignite the injected fuel. This difficulty was overcome by using twin 12V CAV thermostat units in the intake manifold and fitting a 24V starter to give a high cranking speed. With these arrangements cold starting is perfectly satisfactory at temperatures down to 0 °C.

At the other end of the temperature scale is heat. More power means more heat and certain components are subjected to excessive temperatures so that extra local cooling becomes necessary. The most vulnerable parts are the pistons. Very high thermal stresses can be built up in the crown and in the areas of the rings, which can cause such deterioration in the oil that ring sticking occurs. There are a number of ways of dealing with this problem. In the case of the Turbo-Plus engine it was decided to use direct oil cooling and each piston receives a pressurised supply of pre-cooled oil which is squirted into the skirt area at each bottom dead centre position. By this means maximum temperature in the ring-belt area is kept below 280 °C. The system entails the use of a special oil cooler, separate oil pump and additional piping, but it is effective and does not add greatly to weight or cost. A 15 per cent increase in oil-sump capacity is needed, but the standard integral oil pump delivering 8·4 gal/min is retained.

The turbocharger is a Holset 3LD-18/3·04, with larger turbine housing and compressor than the standard model. Delivery is at the rate of 530ft^3 of air/min at 250bhp and 2,450rev/min, at which conditions the delivery pressure is 50in Hg and the pressure ratio 2·6:1. The blower is mounted in the normal way, bolting on to the rear of the exhaust manifold, but because of the increased size of the housing, the heat shield is also larger and so is carried on substantial brackets mounted on the exhaust manifold instead of on the blower.

The intercooler was specially developed, one of the main requirements being that it should be compact. As eventually evolved it has a dry weight of 74lb and stack dimensions 20in length and 7in diameter. Its location is alongside the cylinder head and to accommodate it in this position a new intake manifold was designed to lie beneath the exhaust manifold instead of on top of it, with the result that the Turbo-Plus has an even lower silhouette than the standard version. The materials used in the intercooler are aluminium alloy for the casing, cast iron for the end caps and aluminium and brass for the stack.

The fuel-injection system required modification and a higher output version of the Simms Minimec fuel-injection pump was used. Plungers of 9·5mm diameter, instead of the standard 9mm elements, allowed increased fuel-delivery capacity which at 250bhp is 130mm³/stroke. No change was made in the standard Simms NL 639 fuel injectors, but 2mm pipes replaced the 1·75mm ones to limit line pressures.

Quite extensive changes were made in the new engine's cooling system to increase the capacity which was achieved by using, in the fresh-water system, the same size pump, but fitting a smaller pulley to increase its output from 36 to 50gal/min at 2,450rev/min engine speed.

In the raw-water circuit the same size Jabsco pump was used, but a larger cam gave an increased output of 25gal/min. The components cooled by the two circuits are:

Fresh water: Cylinder block and cylinder head, exhaust manifold water jacket, heater-exchanger tube stack (integral with heater tank) and heat exchanger. No thermostat is used.
Raw water: Intercooler, gearbox oil cooler, engine oil cooler, heat exchanger.

These systems provide ample engine cooling. During development temperature measurements showed that with sea water at

21 °C, cylinder head temperatures were limited to 88 °C and engine oil temperatures to 86 °C.

Turbocharging is not confined to the larger power units. Smaller engines, too, can be stepped up in power output by this method. An example is the Perkins T4.108M marine diesel. This four-cylinder engine is a direct turbocharged development from the normally aspirated 4.108M and an increase in shaft horse power from 49 to 65 at 3,800rev/min is achieved. Again, as in the Ford Turbo-Plus, very little extra weight penalty has been paid, a mere 4·5 per cent increase, well offset by a 21·4 per cent improvement in the power to weight ratio.

Again, of course, the T4.108M is a high revving power unit intended for relatively high-speed craft and when Perkins developed it they particularly had in mind the twin-engine installations in the medium-size fast cruiser range for which these engines can provide high power with low weight and economical fuel consumption.

To achieve the necessary reliability and long working life the Perkins engineers incorporated a number of modifications, although standard components were used wherever possible. Internally, with the exception of the cylinder bores which were increased by 0·0015in, the configuration remained unchanged. Modifications were, however, made to the timing gears, inlet valves, CAV fuel pump drive, pistons, cylinder liners and the 60h nitrided crankshaft. The fuel pump runs in white metal wrapped bushes rather than bronze bushes and because the turbine becomes hot the turbine unit is covered with an asbestos casing. This, and the fact that the amount of flexible piping was considerably reduced, helped to minimise fire risk.

The turbocharger is the Holset 3LD. It is fitted on an extension to the water-cooled exhaust manifold and is trimmed to give 12psig boost. Lubrication is by engine oil from the main pressure rail.

Cylinder pressures in the order of 1,800psig called for fuel injectors with breaking pressures of around 165 atmospheres to withstand the increased thermal loadings.

Blowby from the crankcase resulting from air leakage past

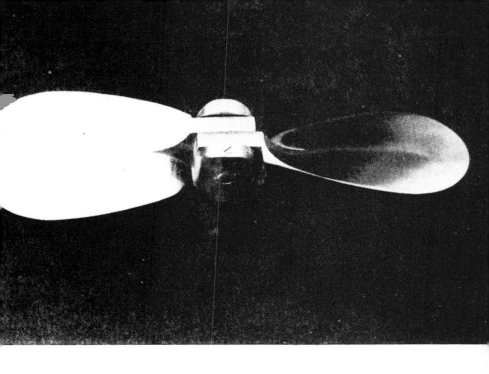

Page 51: 5 (*above*) Hamblematic folding propeller, blades open;
6 (*below*) Hamblematic folding propeller, blades closed

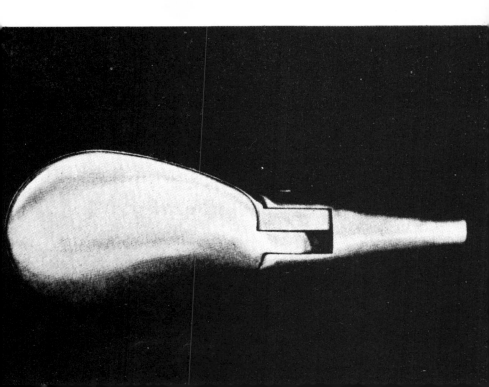

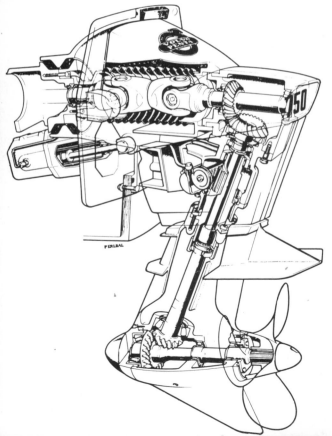

PERLDAL

Page 52: 7 (above)
The Dowty 2-stage,
300mm (12in) water-jet
unit; 8 (left) cutaway
drawing of the Volvo
Penta model 250 outdrive

the turbocharger seals, a problem related to turbocharged engines, was dealt with by connecting the oil-return pipe to the crankcase breather pipe which feeds directly into the turbocharger air intake and so removes air from the oil as it returns to the crankcase.

Oil seals were not needed for either inlet or exhaust valves, good valve guide life without them resulting from the positive pressure in the intake manifold occurring in a turbocharged engine controlling seepage down the valve guides. Normally aspirated engines show a tendency to draw oil down the guides because of the relatively low induction ptessure.

To remove unwanted pulsations from the incoming air charge a new design of inlet manifold was necessary. This was much larger than in the normally aspirated engine and it became possible to locate the intercooler—a sea water/air type—inside the induction manifold, thus both encasing it and ensuring minimum extra weight and reducing engine profile.

Weight saving also resulted from the use of aluminium instead of cast iron for the exhaust manifold with fresh water cooling rather than sea water, eliminating, too, the risk of salt corrosion.

A specially designed elbow in EN 58J stainless steel was provided to deal with the turbocharger exhaust which is cooled by injection of engine-cooling raw water.

Outwardly.the T4.108M looks very little different from the 4.108M but in performance there is a marked change. Expressed as a percentage the power increase is 32.6 per cent, that is the difference between 49shp at 4,000rev/min and 65shp at 3,800rev/min in the turbocharged version. But the improvement has not been obtained at the expense of extra high fuel consumption which only goes up to 3·6gal/hr from 3·25gal/hr and the dry weight (direct drive gearbox) increases only 4·5 per cent from 574lb to 600lb.

These two engines have been dealt with in some detail without going too deeply into the more involved engineering and design considerations, to show how turbocharging with intercooling can provide a worthwhile increase in power output without undue penalties of greatly increased weight, high fuel consumption, unreliability and short life.

CHAPTER 5

ELECTRICAL IGNITION

The ignition system in a petrol engine provides an electric current of high enough voltage to spark between two electrodes at the right time and in so doing ignite the fuel mixture in the cylinders.

The spark occurs at the gap between the sparking plug points when the fuel is at its highest degree of compression and to ensure that it is 'fat' enough a current of at least 14,000–15,000V is necessary. Such current is provided by a magneto or a coil. Essentially, the difference between the two is that the magneto provides a spark without the need for an outside source of current, whereas the coil requires a battery to energise it. Earlier marine engines were often fitted with magnetos and many small auxiliaries, notably the Stuart Turner single- and twin-cylinder units, are still operating with this form of ignition, although coil is available for existing or new engines if required. The magneto is simple and does not involve electric circuitry. For small craft in which electric starting and more sophisticated electric services are not needed, the magneto has advantages, giving a good spark for starting at hand-cranking speeds and being simple to maintain.

However, coil ignition generally gives a fatter spark enabling plug gaps to be larger, a point which is important in two-stroke engines, especially when idling or running slowly for long periods, as when fishing, as this helps to prevent oiling up. Almost all marine engines are fitted with coil ignition because, apart from the better spark, batteries and circuitry for electric starting, navigation and interior lighting and power for electrical navigation equipment, water pumps, heating and refrigeration, and so on, have become standard requirements even in quite small boats.

The spark must occur in each cylinder at precisely the right moment whatever the engine-operating speed may be. To ensure this the system needs a coil and contact breaker to produce the high voltage current, a distributor and high tension cables to convey the current to the cylinders, sparking plugs to provide a gap between two electrodes for the current to spark across and a battery to energise the coil.

The coil works on the principle that momentary interruption of the flow of an electric current in a primary coil will induce high voltage current in a secondary coil located in the primary's magnetic field. An ignition coil consists, therefore, of two windings. The first, or primary, is located around a soft iron core to concentrate the magnetic field and is made up of a few hundred turns of relatively thick wire. The secondary is of much thinner wire wound into thousands of turns. The coil and soft iron core are contained with the necessary insulation inside a metal cylinder having on its top two low-tension terminals and a high-tension terminal with location for the lead to the distributor.

The coil is energised by the battery when the ignition is switched on and the contact breaker points are closed. Current then flows through the primary winding to the contact breaker, via a condenser. The contact breaker, although located in the distributor, is a functional part of the coil, providing the means of interrupting the flow of current in the primary winding. As soon as the points open the primary magnetic field collapses and high-voltage current—around 30,000V in the average coil— is induced in the secondary windings. The contact breaker points open and close for each firing stroke of each cylinder, being operated by a cam having an appropriate number of shoulders or lobes. A condenser is connected across the points to prevent arcing.

The inducement of high voltage in the secondary winding

depends upon a rapid interruption of current flow in the primary and so the contact breaker—and the condenser which also plays a part in this—are important in obtaining consistent high quality ignition. To break the primary circuit quickly and cleanly the points must open instantly and the gap set between them must be correctly maintained as it will tend to decrease as wear takes place in the cam follower. This is particularly noticeable during the running in period of a new engine.

The battery, coil and contact breaker provide high-voltage current which must then be conducted to the sparking plug in the right cylinder at the right time. This is done by the distributor, a unit housing the contact breaker, its operating cam and a rotor arm revolving inside a plastic cap. The cap contains high-tension electrodes and sockets for the HT cable, one for each cylinder. The contact breaker cam and the rotor arm are mounted on the distributor shaft, a spindle driven from the engine camshaft by skew gear. In operation these components are timed so that when the contact breaker points open high-tension current flows to the rotor arm which is in line, but not actually touching, an electrode in the distributor cap. The current then flows through the high-tension cable to the sparking plug where it sparks across the gap between the points. The timing of the spark is, of course, linked to firing stroke in the cylinder.

Basically a sparking plug consists of a central electrode housed within a ceramic insulator and a metal body having a threaded portion to screw into the cylinder head. The second, or negative, electrode is located at the bottom of the threaded portion. Usually plugs are fitted with a thickish ring washer, or gasket, to ensure a gas-tight seal in the cylinder head, but there is also a design with tapered shoulders which, in a suitable machined head, forms a seal without the need of a washer.

When a plug correct for the engine design is screwed into position in the head only the two electrodes and a small portion of the metal at the base of the thread protrude into the combustion chamber. On fitting replacement plugs it is important to use only the type specified by the engine manufacturer so that the reach, or length of thread, is right for the thickness of the particular cylinder head. If too long, a valve or piston might be fouled; if too short, the exposed screw threads in the cylinder head would carbon up and it might be impossible later to fit the correct length of plug.

Apart from these risks the use of wrong plugs could lower engine performance by altering the designed position of the firing point which is as much a design factor as the size, area and shape of the combustion chamber, direction and rate of gas flow and temperatures and mixture strengths.

Also plugs are ranged from hot to cold which is an expression of their ability to conduct heat away from the sparking point of the centre electrode. This is controlled by the length of the insulator, which is long for hot plugs and short for cold plugs, with variations between these extremes. Basically hot plugs are used in cooler-running engines of the lower performance type, whereas cold plugs, which conduct heat away quickly, are fitted in higher-performance engines. Hot plugs tend to burn off deposits and so can be useful in engines required to run at slow speeds for considerable periods.

In operation the high-tension current enters the plug at the top terminal, travels down the centre electrode and sparks across the gap to the earthed electrode. The size of the gap varies between about 0·020 and 0·040in and is usually set at around 0·025in.

Continual sparking from the main electrode tip gradually wears away the metal so that checking and resetting plug gaps should be routine maintenance. Plugs also accumulate various deposits and should be cleaned regularly. Dirt and oil contaminating the exterior can also lower plug performance.

CHAPTER 6

ELECTRICAL INSTALLATIONS

PART I

There are two main factors in considering a ship's electrical installation: the supply of current and the means of conveying it to the electrical appliances. The way these matters are handled has a direct bearing on the safety of craft and crew.

The source of current supply varies. In a large yacht or working craft the engine room may contain, in addition to the main propulsion engine, a smaller engine whose sole task is to drive an electric generator. In such a case a typical arrangement would be that the propulsion engine drives a generator charging batteries used solely for engine starting, with perhaps small additional loadings such as navigation lights and the odd cabin, wheelhouse and compass light, while the smaller engine drives a generator providing 230/240V ac current for domestic purposes such as cooking, refrigeration, water- and space-heating, ship's and navigation instruments such as radar, ship's machinery such as winches, hoist and other high-powered equipment, with circuitry covering rectifiers for dc equipment and arranged to connect to shore mains supply when berthed.

In other installations reliance may be placed solely on the main propulsion engine to provide electrical generation for engine-starting batteries and, separately, ship's and domestic supplies. Yet again, a portable generator unit may be used for charging the ship's and domestic supply batteries if the load taken from them is normally beyond the capacity of the propuslion engine's generator.

Electrical Installations

In smaller boats the propulsion engine's generator often provides sufficient capacity for adequate charging of starter and supply batteries or, in sailing craft using the engine only infrequently, a small portable dc generator may be used. In still smaller craft, in which perhaps current is only required for engine starting, navigation lights, a few interior lights and compass illumination, the engine's generator will be adequate for all normal usage of the vessel.

Finally there is the craft which has no current-generating facilities, the engine being hand-started and navigation and interior lights burning oil. It may be decided to install electric lighting for convenience and for this purpose wiring and electric fitments are installed and power is supplied by a battery which is taken ashore for recharging when necessary.

Whatever the system, whenever electricity is brought aboard a boat there are two potential dangers—corrosion caused by electrolytic action and fire, caused by spark or short circuit. It is for these reasons that ship-borne electric circuitry should be designed and installed in accordance with the recommendations of authorities such as the SBBNF and electrical equipment manufacturers and that all wiring, fitments and apparatus should, wherever applicable, meet British Standards Institution specifications.

In the matter of marine electrics Lucas/CAV are 'a boat user's best friend'. They publish a wealth of information on the numerous aspects of installations and, of course, supply all the components and equipment. Their marine division operating from Acton offers a comprehensive advisory service to engine manufacturers, boat builders, yacht yards and private and professional owners. If anyone has any queries, or is planning electrical installations in a boat, he should seek their advice. I do not wish to overemphasise this, but getting boat electrics right is of prime importance and there is still a great deal of ignorance, even in professional quarters, about the whole subject.

The approach to the electrical installation must be as a whole concept. It is quite inadequate to think in terms of having a battery good enough for engine starting and then add in other equipment on a random basis. Even in small boats some electrical services are expected and the engine manufacturer's recommendations on battery capacity are naturally related to engine starting and the capacity of the standard generator. In large private craft electrical services are often expected to be no less than those in houses with additional electrically operated items such as showers and WCs. As already mentioned, professional craft often use electrically driven machinery and equipment. The marine electrical installation must therefore be thought of as a system, depending for its safety, efficiency and reliability on the choice of suitable items of equipment, the location of such items and the methods of their fitment.

What are the basic considerations? These can best be analysed if it is assumed that a new installation is being planned, rather than that equipment is to be added to existing circuitry. Either way the principles are the same, but in the latter case there can be greater problems, the only acceptable solution to which may be to tear everything out and start again.

An average installation will consist of a battery, or batteries, giving current for engine starting and general services and these will be charged by the main engine or an auxiliary engine. With the present trend towards the use of alternators rather than dynamos it may well be that only larger craft with relatively heavy demands on the electrical supply will have auxiliary engines for charging, but the relative merits of dynamo and alternator will be discussed later.

At once the planner is faced with the necessity to try and decide on all the services required before designing the circuit in detail. This is because batteries age both with use and when not in use, and even if they are not over worked the effect of continual discharging and recharging will gradually reduce their efficiency and eventually wear them out. This process will be accelerated if they are overloaded, as may happen when equipment is added to the circuit over and above that originally planned. It is therefore less expensive, apart from more technically desirable, to calculate the total battery capacity and allow for adequate charging facilities at the design stage. This is not a difficult process, as will be seen. The greatest problem is more likely to be met in making sure that every electrical service required when the craft is in commission is thought of during planning.

Then consideration must be given to wiring layout and the desirability of keeping cables as short as possible, a factor which affects the positioning of switchboards, batteries and control boards. When engine spaces are restricted in size accessibility of equipment is often a problem, but it is of the utmost importance to provide maximum facilities for inspection and maintenance of equipment.

Cables must be of the correct type for marine use, stranded copper with insulation, and adequately rated for the planned duties and mechanically protected wherever necessary. Switches, fuses and accessories must also be marine type, adequately rated and if fitted in positions exposed to salt and spray they must be of waterproof construction and non-corrosive. Ferrous metal fittings in exposed positions will inevitably corrode and fail.

Marine electrical systems must be wired as insulated return, that is, using two insulated cables. The practice of earthing either the positive or negative poles of generators and starter motors leads, in the case of insulation failure on the opposite pole, to short circuit conditions or leakage of current which can result in electrolytic action on tanks, pipes, electrical and underwater equipment.

Adequate ventilation is of prime importance. Batteries give off hydrogen, adding another hazardous element to domestic gases, exhaust fumes and fuel vapours. Explosion danger is very real from arcing of brush commutators in unsuitable fan motors and where such equipment is used in automatic ventilation systems fan motors must be totally enclosed and control switches and relays, when fitted near batteries or immediately below gas fires and cookers, must also be totally enclosed and non-arcing.

It may be possible to obtain efficient ventilation by natural air flow, particularly when the boat is moving. On the principle that heated air expands and rises and in doing so induces a flow of cold air as replacement, ducting may be arranged in such a way that this natural function acts in a controlled way to provide the necessary ventilation. However, if such a system is only operative when the craft is underway, it will be only partially satisfactory and a fan-induced air flow should be installed.

Such a system should not be confined to the electrical apparatus only, but should be designed to ventilate any other equipment which can fail through overheating such as generators, batteries and control boards, and for general ventilation through the whole boat.

While still on general requirements for efficient and safe marine electrical installation, interference may be mentioned. This can affect, sometimes severely, echo sounders, radio apparatus, radar and other electronic apparatus and it is necessary to control such interference so as to either remove it or reduce it to tolerable levels.

The foregoing shows the need in general terms for a calculated approach to the installation of marine electrical equipment. Before looking at the requirements in more detail, with a close examination of the measures needed to prevent electrolytic corrosion and electrical interference, there are two other spheres to be considered because of their importance in subsequent calculations and management of the eventual installations. These are batteries and generators. Both divide sharply into two separate categories. Batteries may be lead acid or alkaline. The choice of types and their management and maintenance is dealt with fully in the next chapter, only capacity being discussed here. Generators may be either dynamos or alternators. The differences and the advantages and disadvantages between the two will be discussed in this chapter.

A systematic approach to the electrical installation is essential and if the various factors are dealt with in the following sequence the result will be a sound, safe and efficient system.

The first task is to determine the total electrical loading, that is the total combined power needed for every item of current-consuming equipment. This is expressed in watts. The flow of electric current, on the other hand, is expressed in amperes and a battery (a source of supply of current) has a capacity expressed in ampere hours, that is to say, if it were discharged at a steady rate of so many amps it would last so many hours before becoming discharged. It is usual to convert watts into amperes which is done simply by dividing the total wattage of the system by the system voltage. For example, a total loading of 240W on a 12V system = 240 divided by 12 = 20A. Or 240W divided by 24V = 10A.

In calculating an imaginary electrical installation a 24V system will be assumed, but the amperage would be arrived at in the same way, whether the system was on 12 or 32V, or on 230/240 if all the equipment being dealt with was powered by an alternating current (ac) generator. Battery-operated systems are, of course, on direct current (dc).

All the equipment required is listed as in the following example:

Lighting: 24 points at 20W = 480W
Navigation lights: 4 at 12W = 48W
Refrigerator: 1 at 180W = 180W
Radiotelephone: 1 at 60W = 60W
Radar: 1 at 350W = 350W
Vent fans: 2 at 48W = 96W
Pumps: 3 at 48W = 144W
To which may be added sundry loads such as:
Searchlights ⎫
Echo sounder ⎪
Aldis lamp ⎪
Compass lights ⎬ = 120W
Windscreen wiper ⎪
 or Kent ⎪
'Clearview' ⎭

Added together these items produce a maximum load of 1,478W which, divided by the voltage—24—gives 61·5A.

It is probably unlikely that every electrical component will be called into use at any one time, but calculation of maximum load is necessary to arrive at a correct relationship between the average and the greatest possible demand, so that adequate generator capacity is provided. Maximum loading also controls the size of cables and switches, as will be seen later. In making the calculation special equipment, or that in only occasional use, such as power winches, may be ignored.

With maximum total loading known, which will naturally vary from craft to craft according to different owners' individual requirements, a further calculation is made to determine battery capacity. In this case an average demand through a period of 24hr is taken, covering the operation of the vessel while at sea and in harbour and assuming a 24V general services battery.

Lighting: 6 lights at 20W for 6hr = 720Wh
Navigation: 4 lights at 12W for 4hr= 192Wh
Refrigerator: 1 at 180W for 8hr = 1,440Wh
Radiotelephone: 1 at 60W for 2hr = 120Wh
Radar: 1 at 350W for 4hr = 1,400Wh
Vent fans: 2 at 48W for 4hr = 384Wh
Pumps: 3 at 48W for 1hr = 144Wh
Sundry loads: at 120W for 1hr = 120Wh

The total power consumption is therefore 4,520Wh, which at 24V equals approximately 188Ah.

Provided a separate, adequate capacity, battery were used for engine starting, about which more will be said later, a suitable general service battery would be one of 250Ah capacity, provided battery charging took place within every 24hr period. If charging was possible at only 48hr intervals, the capacity would have to be doubled—to 500Ah.

If single-starting loads and other electrical services are to be operated from a single battery, extra capacity must be added according to the engine manufacturer's recommendations on battery size. This system is only suitable, however, for the very simplest electrical installations, such as are normally confined to small boats, consisting of, say, two or three low-wattage cabin lights, navigation lights and perhaps a compass light, in addition to engine-starting requirements. Even in this type of craft a separate, adequate capacity engine starting battery would be strongly recommended if extensive passage-making at night was a regular occurrence.

The reason for this emphasis on separate batteries for engine starting is sound enough. Engine-starter motors are not constructed for continuous rating. This means that if their life is to be prolonged the engine must be got going quickly. Failure in this respect ensures expensive starter-motor repairs or replacement because slow cranking causes dangerously high current flow in the motor and this happens whenever starting is attempted on a partially run down battery.

If a battery on an average engine-starting circuit has to supply current for other electrical equipment except on a purely occasional basis, more will be taken from it than can be replaced by the charging system working under normal engine-operating conditions. When this happens the terminal voltage to the starter motor drops and trouble starts.

Having arrived at maximum loadings and determined adequate battery capacity, the next calculation is made to ascertain generator capacity. This must be sufficient to carry the average load and the charge rate appropriate to the batteries used and the temperature and other environmental conditions in which they normally operate. These requirements are dealt with fully in Chapter 7 ('Batteries'). If the total output current of the charging source is only equal to, or less than, that taken by the normal load, the battery will be discharged. And it must be remembered, in calculating generator output, to take into consideration the normal, expected engine speed and the usual time of running, that is, whether the boat is used under power, daily, weekly or only occasionally at well-spaced weekends. If engine-running time is insufficient, related to the required use of the electrical services, either greater battery capacity must be installed, a separate generator must be used, or batteries must be taken ashore regularly for charging.

Generator capacity is arrived at by making two more calculations, or three if the loads when the craft is at sea differ considerably from those when in harbour.

First, the load in amperes must be found and from the previous example given for a 24V system the figures are:

	Load (A)
Lighting:	5
Navigation:	2
Refrigerator:	7·5
Radiotelephone:	2·5
Radar:*	14·5
Vent fans:	4
Pumps:	6
Sundry loads:	5
Total	46·5

To this total must now be added the battery charge rate which is calculated as follows:

$$\text{Rate} = \frac{C}{T} \times 1\cdot4$$

where C = battery capacity in ampere hours, T = charging time in hours, $1\cdot4$ = factor for battery efficiency (approx. 70 per cent).

Thus, in the example taken, using a 250Ah battery operating at 24V,

*There are several radars now available which, designed specifically for smaller craft, use considerably less current. One, the Electronic Laboratories Seascan, is rated at only 48W and requires a mere 2 amperes on a 24V system. There are other sets which require less than 100W and under 200W. The appropriate figure for the equipment in use should be therefore substituted in the loadings calculations.

$$*10\text{hr rate} = \frac{250}{10} \times 1\cdot 4 = 35\text{A}$$

35A must therefore be added to the previous 46·5A and the total load becomes 81·5A.

The 81·5A, then, is the required generator output at *normal engine speeds*. To achieve this it is necessary to decide on the type of generator and the way in which it will be driven. (In these examples it is assumed that the generator will be driven by the main propulsion engine. The method of calculation would be just the same if the propulsion engine charged only its own starting battery and a separate, non-propelling engine powered a separate generating unit, which might be in portable form, or a permanent installation.)

The two types of generator are, of course, the dynamo and the alternator. Both are attached to the engine and driven by it, and both generate alternating current which they convert to direct current, but the methods by which they do this differ. The dynamo converts ac to dc mechanically by means of commutator and brushes, while the alternator uses diodes (electronic valves) for this purpose.

The alternator, besides being smaller in size and lighter in weight than the dynamo of similar output, is a good deal more efficient and, because it has a very wide speed range, can give high current output at low engine speeds. Also, because of the absence of commutator, maintenance requirements are virtually negligible. Yet another advantage is that it may be rotated in either direction, which means simplification in methods of mounting and driving.

Most alternators are self-limiting in current output and require only voltage control. Large machines which do not have current-limiting characteristics are fitted with current/voltage regulators. Various arrangements may be used in alternator installations,

*An explanation of how a '10hr rate' is arrived at will be found in Chapter 7 ('Batteries').

such as the connection of similar voltage and drive ratio units in parallel or singly to charge a single battery or, by the use of an auxiliary battery-isolating device, a single alternator may charge two batteries.

Without doubt the alternator is appreciably superior to the dynamo for marine use because of its flexibility, small dimensions and ability to provide high current output at low engine speeds. Dynamos are, of course, perfectly adequate for small craft in which demands for electricity supplies are low.

Returning, then, to the question of generator type and output, selection of a suitable unit must be made from the range available, using the manufacturer's published information sheets, which also give details of suitable mounting arrangements. These are readily available to owners, boatbuilders, designers and naval architects. But the drive pulley *ratio* has to be selected for the individual application in each case. This requires information from the engine manufacturer (usually published in data sheet form) giving minimum engine speed for normal running. Then, from the generator data sheet the maximum load speed and the maximum safe operating speed are obtained.

With these two sets of information available the pulley ratio to produce a generator speed at which maximum generator output is given at something above minimum engine speed. If vibrating contact regulators are used the normal running speed must be at least 20 per cent higher than the maximum load speed to prevent the contacts being damaged by prolonged running on maximum field current.

In a practical application the pulley ratio would have to be rechecked to ensure that at maximum engine speed the generator was not overspeeded. If this did happen the remedy would be to either change the pulley ratio, which would mean having to accept a lower generator output, or select a more suitable generator. An example of pulley ratio selection will make the procedure clear and for this data from the power curve of a typical alternator, the CAV AC90, can be used in conjunction with the previously calculated output requirement of 81·5A.

Page 69: 9 (*left*) The Enfield Mk2 Z-drive transom unit; 10 (*below*) cutaway drawing of the Scania hydrop drive unit

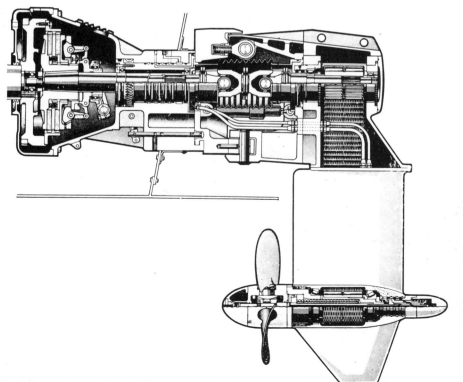

Page 70: 11 (*above*) The Farymann 'A' 10hp diesel engine, suitable for use with the Hydromarin drive (see below); 12 (*below*) the Hydromarin diesel-hydraulic drive, suitable for use with the Farymann 'A' 10hp engine (see above)

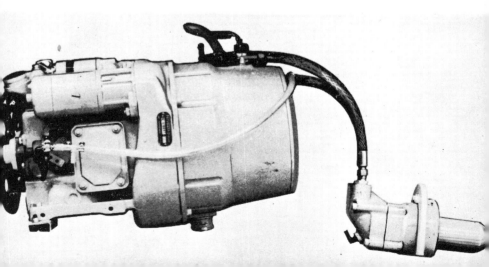

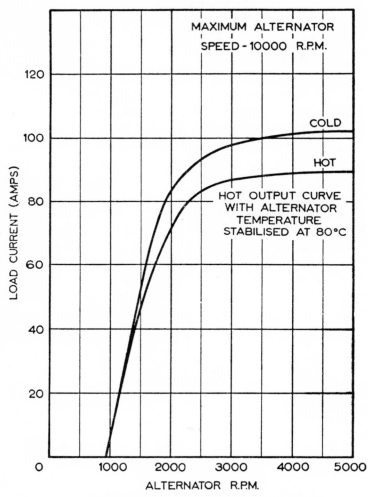

PERFORMANCE OF AC 90 AT 27·5 VOLTS

Fig 5   AC 90 alternator performance curve

From the AC90 performance curve (Fig 5) it will be seen that
this output is obtained at a generator speed of 2,500rev/min.
Operating speeds of a typical medium-sized marine engine
would be:

	Speed (rev/min)
Idling:	450
Low speed cruise:	850
Maximum cruise (average):	1,500
Maximum speed (continuous):	1,850
Emergency speed (say 30min):	2,150

The minimum engine speed is the low speed cruise at 850rev/min and the alternator speed of 2,500rev/min is therefore divided by this figure, ie 2,500 ÷ 850 = 3, approximately. Thus a pulley ratio of 3:1 is required.

This ratio is then checked to ensure that at emergency engine speed the maximum safe alternator speed of 10,000rev/min (obtained from the performance curve) is not exceeded, and this is simply a matter of multiplying the 2,150rev/min by 3, ie 2,150 × 3 = 6,450rev/min, which is well within the limit.

The table below shows generator outputs at various speeds and makes it clear that the 3:1 pulley ratio is correct.

Engine speed	(rev/min)	Alternator speed (rev/min)	Alternator output (A)
Idling	450	1,350	30
Low speed cruise	850	2,550	83
Maximum cruise (average)	1,500	4,500	90
Maximum speed (continuous)	1,850	5,550	90
Emergency speed (30min)	2,150	6,450	90

The installation of a generator is not a complicated matter, either when fitting for the first time to an existing engine, as for example when converting from hand to electric starting and/or installing electric services in the boat, or from the maintenance point of view when the unit is already installed, as on a new engine.

Driving belts must be correctly tensioned to the manufacturer's specifications. If too loose they will slip and cause reduction of output and excessive wear. If too tight they put an unnecessary strain on the generator bearings which can cause overheating and, again, lowered performance and excessive wear. Belts must also run true and centrally round the pullies which means correct alignment of the components. Belts usually stretch after an initial running-in period and need checking for tension within a few hours. After that they settle down and, provided they are running true, require very little adjustment.

Generators should be kept away from hot spots and if necessary protected from spray and moisture. And bonding to a common earth—by means of a short flexible earth strap—is necessary if radiotelephone or other electronic equipment is aboard.

Control boards are an essential part of the generating installation. Dynamos are now generally controlled by current/voltage systems, which give quick battery charging without overloading the generator, by means of a current regulator which allows a predetermined maximum output at a constant rate until the battery voltage equals what it would be if the battery was fully charged. Then the voltage regulator holds a constant voltage and gradually reduces the charge rate to a trickle charge. In installations using two dynamos in parallel circulating could result in nil charge from one and varying output from the other. To prevent this a balancing winding must be incorporated in the control board. Older installations using a dynamo may be equipped with a compensated voltage system.

The dynamo will continue to be found in many earlier marine installations, but it is now virtually replaced by the alternator on new equipment. In fact CAV Lucas, the main UK manufacturer of generating machinery, no longer offer dynamos for marine purposes, although they continue the necessary spares service.

Self-limiting current output alternators such as the AC90 may be operated in parallel without balancing circuits because circulating currents cannot flow and load sharing is unnecessary because these units cannot be overloaded. Cutouts are not required because the rectifying diodes prevent reverse battery current flow when the alternators are at rest and due to the self-limiting current output feature the regulator has only to control voltage.

Fully transistorised, totally enclosed control boards containing no working parts and requiring no maintenance are fitted with some alternators. The CAV 440 regulator is a typical example. In this silicon semiconductors protect against high ambient temperatures and there is a choice of three voltage settings to enable the charge rate to be adjusted to suit the user's requirements.

There are certain precautions to be taken in the installation and use of alternators. Advance field-switching contacts in the battery-isolating switch, or surge protection units, should be used to prevent the alternator being open circuited without prior de-energising of the field. If this is not done a surge would damage the rectifying diodes and could also harm the regulator.

Indiscriminate switching of field connections should be avoided for the following reasons: glazing of commutator and slip rings is caused by continuous open circuit operation; contact life is shortened by additional resistance in the regulator circuit resulting from extended leads to switches; and extended leads increase the possibility of radio-interference.

The manufacturer's instructions on testing should be followed exactly because the semiconductors used in alternators and regulators are voltage sensitive and can be ruined if tested with a 'megger'-type insulation tester.

Alternators and some transistorised regulators can be damaged immediately and beyond repair by reverse polarity connections to the battery. As a protection against this reverse polarity protection units are available for some equipment.

On completion of an installation all the electrical equipment should be run for a time before the application of an insulation test, in order to allow for a rise in temperature.

That an approved system of distribution of current should be used is of prime importance. The risk potential of an incorrectly carried out electrical installation in a boat cannot be too highly stressed. Again, there are methods approved by the SBBNF and the electrical equipment manufacturers and these should be followed precisely, the work being carried out by, or finally checked and approved by, a competent *marine* electrical engineer. The principal requirements are: the system should be insulated return, the feed being from a main switchboard through switches and fuses rated to correspond to the maximum rating of the outgoing circuit conductors; separate, identified fuses must be used to provide short-circuit protection for all individual circuits such as general lighting, ventilating, heating, radio and lights and components; switchboards and fuseboards must be placed in positions where they can be got at readily and enclosed in metal containers if necessary. If wooden containers are used they should be lined with fireproof material.

Either the totally enclosed powder-filled cartridge or the rewirable type of fuse may be used. The latter type must be loaded with only a single strand of the correct gauge fuse wire to comply with the rating normally given on the fuse carrier. It is never wise to fit anything but the specified gauge of fuse wire. If it is too thin it may not carry the circuit's normal load without blowing and if it is too thick it may not blow when it should, allowing a defective, or potentially dangerous, fault to go undetected. A fuse is, after all, an automatic cutout switch which prevents a continuing flow of current to a defect, perhaps a short circuit, which could lead to fire. If a fuse blows, and the cause is unknown, a full investigation of the circuit should be made at once. If no fault can be found, but a replacement fuse wire blows again when the current is switched on, the circuit should be switched out until it can be tested by an electrical engineer. Never, in such circumstances, should a heavier gauge fuse wire be put in, however inconvenient the loss of the circuit may be to those on board.

A point worth noting is that not all fuses are rated in the same way. Lucas and CAV fuses, for example, are rated at the 'blowing' figure, that is, a 25A fuse will blow at 25A and will carry 12½A. Some other manufacturers rate a 25A fuse to carry 25A and blow at a higher figure. It is important, therefore, to be sure which system of rating is used, checking with the manufacturer if necessary.

Fuse wire is tinned copper wire, and, because it is affected by atmospheric and temperature changes, will in time deteriorate and so may blow at a lower loading than the rating indicated.

When circuits are being planned it is wise to provide spare circuits on the fuseboard to allow for later additions. If this is not done there is risk of overloading existing circuits by adding more services or equipment to them.

Switchboards should be of high dielectric insulating material such as Bakelite and if they are metal faced all the parts carrying current must be insulated, with all live connections being made at the back of the panel.

The ring main system may be used in marine electrical installations. It offers certain advantages in that additions can be made easily without the risk of overloading individual circuits and connections may be made at the nearest convenient point, while local cable runs are kept short. Connections for lighting sockets, pumps and auxiliary circuits, made through intermediate junction points, may have the protection of fuses or thermal overload trips. The ring main consists of a two-core cable running continuously from the isolator along one side of the craft and returning to it along the other side, thus forming a continuous loop fed at both ends.

PART II

The cables and wiring used in marine electrical installation must be of the correct types for the duties they have to perform and it is important that a new system should be approved by an appropriate authority at the planning stage. On taking over a new craft the owner should seek a guarantee that the work has been done to an approved specification. On buying a secondhand craft it is wise to have the whole electrical system examined at the survey, or later by a competent electrical engineer. These are safety precautions and they cannot be over emphasised. The reasons are plain enough on analysis of exactly what cables and wires have to do. Electrical energy may be likened to water, insofar as it will flow along a conductor. As with water, the flow must be created by pressure. If, by exerting excessive pressure, attempts were made to force more water through a pipe of given diameter than it could properly convey, it would burst. The same failure would happen if the pipe was too small for the duty required. Or if fracture did not occur there would be excessive resistance to the water flow.

Although they are conductors of electrical energy, rather than a liquid, electric cables and wires may be thought of as pipes. In section they are, of course, solid rather than hollow and the electricity flows through the solid. But, like the pipe, it must be protected by an outer casing to keep it in the right place and stop it diverging to any other convenient conductor, either by direct contact, or by jumping a gap in the form of a spark, in either case causing a potentially dangerous situation.

The cable, or wire, conductor, therefore, must be large enough to carry the required amount of current and it must be sheathed and insulated to ensure that the electricity is properly contained and there is no danger of leakage to adjacent objects.

Cable and wire sizes for various duties and loads are readily available in tabulated form from manufacturers of electrical equipment such as CAV/Lucas, or authorities like the SBBNF and Lloyds. Reference should always be made to these when planning an installation or rewiring an existing one. Heavy-duty conductors, such as those from battery to engine starter, are normally referred to as cables, those with lighter loadings, as wires. Or in some cases the whole installation is described as the wiring, with the individual conductors described as cables. For simplicity the term cable will here be used to refer to any type of wiring.

For marine use cables should be of approved manufacture, of a suitable grade and of the stranded copper type. Although solid conductors are used by many Continental boatbuilders, they are not approved by United Kingdom authorities. Cables must be sheathed and insulated, suitable materials being as follows:

Insulation:
Polyvinylchloride compound (PVC)
Rubber
Butyl rubber compound
Mineral

Sheathing:
Cotton-covered flameproof braided (FPB)
Lead or copper
Polychloroprene (PCP)
Metallic flexible tubing
Tinned copper braid

Of these materials, PVC compound, being a thermoplastic, is affected by heat and should not be subjected to temperatures above 50 °C (122 °F); PCP is flame resistant; Butyl rubber compound has good water-heat and insulating resistance and sheathed with flameproof braiding it is approved for engine wiring.

A good combination for all general wiring is PVC-insulated cable sheathed with PCP.

Very high resistance to heat and great mechanical strength are characteristics of Mineral-insulated cables, but satisfactory installation is more difficult (and therefore more costly) and, because the magnesium oxide insulation is water absorbent, the ends of metallic sheathing must be sealed.

The installation of cables must comply with laid down requirements. Firm fixing at regular intervals, or enclosure in some form of mechanical protection, is necessary. They may be fixed to wooden battens with brass saddles and screws, or carried through a trough of square or rectangular PVC, or be secured to a perforated carrier tray, or enclosed in galvanised conduit.

There are also conditions governing the methods used in running cables through different parts of the ship, all of which are concerned with safety. Watertight glands must be used when cables pass through watertight bulkheads. Each side of the gland the cable should be formed in a short loop to prevent tension and possible fracture.

Running cables under floors and behind fuel tanks should always be avoided if possible. If not possible they must be protected by galvanised conduit, which must also be used if cables have to pass through tank spaces, in which case the conduit must be earthed and bonded.

The tables referred to on page 77 give cable sizes and ratings suitable for small craft. These are based on the resistance of the conductor and the permissible temperature rise in the insulation. It is the type of insulation which governs the maximum continuous rating.

An important factor in small-craft electrical systems is voltage drop, and when calculating this the total length of cable in the circuit must be included, that is, both live and return. Voltage drop is related to the electrical resistance of the conductor. The greater its diameter, the lower is the resistance. This factor is used when calculating the required cable size for a particular application. Excessive voltage drop will lower the efficiency of electrical equipment such as pumps, motors, battery chargers, navigation instruments and lights and, even more important perhaps, reduce the operating capacity of the engine starter motor. It is therefore desirable that the drop does not exceed 4 per cent of battery voltage in any specific circuit. This equals about 0·5V in a 12V circuit and 1V in a 24V circuit.

In calculating voltage drop use Ohm's Law, which states that:

$E = 1 \times R$ when E = voltage drop,
1 = current in amps and
R = total resistance to the cable in the circuit.

Examples will show how this law is worked out and from it the relationship between conductor size, maximum rating, resistance and voltage drop can be seen.

2 × single-core PVC cables, each 15ft in length, are required to carry a load of 30A at 24V. An appropriate table shows that 7/·044 PVC is rated at 31A. The table also shows the cable resistance in Ω/ft of length, in this case 0·00079. So, we have:

$$E = 1 \times R\,(R = 2 \times 15 \times 0\cdot00079)$$
$$= 30 \times 0\cdot0237$$
$$= 0\cdot711V$$

or

2 × single-core PVC cables, each 30ft in length, are required to carry a load of 30A at 24V.

$$E = 1 \times R\,(R = 2 \times 30 \times 0\cdot00079)$$
$$= 30 \times 0\cdot0474$$
$$= 1\cdot422V$$

In both these examples the 7/·044 cable is within the rating requirement, but in the second example the voltage drop is greater than the recommended 1V and so a larger cable should be used. The second example also emphasises the importance of using engine starter motor cables of adequate size and keeping them as short as possible. Starter circuits carry high amperage. A 1V drop in a circuit carrying 500A, for instance, means a loss of 0·67hp (nearly ¾hp) and in low temperature this could mean failure to start.

It will be appreciated from the foregoing that, as always in marine work, a methodical approach, backed by approved practices and authoritative information, will ensure satisfactory results and a feeling of security. Simply using any bits of wire that happen to be around in the bosun's locker just will not do.

The minimum engine control instrumentation recommended by the SBBNF is ignition switch for coil ignition with warning light if required; stop switch for magneto cutout on magneto ignition engines; and a stop cable or solenoid button for diesel engines. For engines fitted with charging generators there should be a charge/discharge ammeter.

Further recommended instruments, particularly for high-speed engines, are engine oil-pressure gauge or warning light, water-temperature gauge or warning light and, for oil-operated gearboxes, a reverse gear-pressure gauge or oil-warning light.

Normally such instrumentation will be supplied by the engine manufacturer as standard equipment, but when additional instruments are to be added, or where the user is providing his own instrumentation, it is necessary to have evidence that they are suitable for marine use and capable of withstanding vibration and shock. A qualified marine engineer should advise if there is any doubt. Unsuitable or false-functioning engine instruments could put the craft in hazard.

Finally, in conclusion of Part II of this chapter, brief consideration must be given to a factor affecting the operation of electrical equipment, as well, of course, as other mechanical components, including the engine or auxiliary engine. The factor is temperature. Any conductor of electricity resists the flow of electrical current to some degree. Good conductors offer least resistance, poor ones the most resistance. Current is absorbed by this resistance and converted into heat, so that any electrical machine or conductor is flowing, and any such equipment will have a continuous rating which is reached when the generated heat equals the heat loss.

In order to assess, or limit, the temperature rise in equipment it is necessary to relate the operating temperature rise to the ambient temperature, that is, the temperature of the surrounding air. For example, if a machine temperature of 100 °C (212 °F) is recorded in an ambient temperature of 30 °C (86 °F) the temperature rise is 70 °C (126 °F), or if the same machine operates in an ambient temperature of 45 °C (113 °F) the machine temperature will be 115 °C (239 °F). If there is any doubt about the machine-operating temperature, either because the rating is unknown, or the ambient temperature is thought to be excessively high, the equipment manufacturer or a qualified marine engineer or marine electrician should be consulted. In assessing temperature rise in electrical equipment and cabling the rating should always be according to the maximum ambient temperature obtaining at normal operating conditions.

Excessive ambient temperatures in confined engine spaces which cannot, or are not, properly ventilated, and where dynamos, alternators, batteries, control boards and wiring have to be placed at or near hot spot areas, or adjacent to engines which themselves operate at relatively high temperatures, can cause overheating problems with some equipment, but these problems are today being reduced or contained by the use of silicon semiconductors in control boards and new insulating materials in alternators.

In summary, the marine electrical equipment obtainable today, backed by the manufacturer's advice and service facilities, will be efficient and reliable in operation provided the components used in the installation are correctly chosen and fitted.

PART III

Radio interference and electrolytic corrosion

Any craft having an electrical installation can suffer from interference with radio- and direction-finding equipment and electronic navigation aids, whether the installation be a Dynastart on a small boat, or the full sophistication expected in the large pleasure or working craft.

What happens is that unwanted radio-frequency energy is generated by the vessel's electrical equipment and picked up by the receiver aerial system. The signals transmitted by radio-stations are intelligent, but those spontaneously generated on board are not, and the radio and other equipment cannot discriminate between the two if they both have a common frequency and are of similar strength. The result is the loss of the intelligent signal in the random noise.

The ship-generated radio-frequency energy is caused by abruptly varying or interrupting the flow of current in a conductor. This happens in the normal operation of marine electrical equipment of all types, as, for example, in the switching of generator fields, the action of commutators in dynamos and electric motors and in switches and thermostats.

Often the main source of interference is the engine-driven dynamo, or alternator, and their associated control boards, but the trouble can come also from ignition systems, fluorescent light fittings, and voltage and current regulators of the vibrating type, and from the transistorised units which have come into increasing use.

While it is sometimes claimed that the alternator is less likely to be a source of interference than the dynamo, this is not necessarily so. Although the alternator's slip rings and brushes conduct field excitation current of some 2–3A and this can compare favourably with the dynamo commutator and brushes which carry the total output current, the alternator's rectifying diodes, which handle output current, may produce just as much interference as the commutator and brush combination.

Much the same comments apply when comparing vibrating and transistorised regulators because, while vibrating contacts are often very noisy, transistors are switching devices and so can cause interference.

There are two main ways in which this generated radio frequency energy is conveyed to radio equipment—conduction and radiation. In the former the conducted component flows directly from the source to the radio through the wiring system which itself can then become a number of aerials each radiating the interference signals. In the latter the radiated interference can be picked up and reradiated by wiring, metal fittings, wire stays and similar components, each of which adds to and so increases the total radiated interference.

What action then can be taken to guard against this interference? There are four main recommendations:

(i) Location of the aerial and lead in as far away as possible from the electromagnetic influences.

(ii) Tune the aerial efficiency to give the best possible signal to noise ratio.

(iii) Keep radio supply mains as short as possible and running as far away as possible from electrical machinery. Use the correct specification cable to ensure minimum voltage drop.

(iv) Position the radio as far away as is possible from interference sources and earth it with a low-impedance conductor to a common point such as the main engine.

Individual equipments generating radio interference are dealt with by the use of capacitors and inductors. These are positioned as close as possible to the interference source to lessen the risk of conduction and radiation. Although they work in different ways the capacitor and the inductor may be used together to form what is known as a filter. Either singly or together they confine radio frequency energy to small, non-radiating circuits. The capacitor provides a low impedance path to radio frequency currents which are thus shunted or bypassed to earth. The inductor, on the other hand, filters or blocks these currents by presenting them with a high impedance.

Although generators and control boards are available with capacitors and inductors connected to the generator output and control circuits and may be effective, particularly if used in conjunction with screened cables, the only really satisfactory suppression system is that which meets the full requirements of British Standard BS1597/1963 which lays down the permissible limits of interference over the frequency range of 15kc to 300Mc. The casual use of capacitors connected in the generator field circuit is not to be recommended because this method seriously shortens the life of vibrating-type regulator contacts.

The BS standard can be met on all radio-equipped craft by screening and filtering. Two CAV systems, the 423 and the 446, meet the requirements. Each consists of a screened metal box enclosing the control board and containing the filter units; a length of screened metallic braiding through which the inter-connecting cables are run between the alternator or dynamo and the control board; a screened ferrule entry to alternator or dynamo.

Provided these two systems are properly installed they will provide a successful solution to radio interference associated with alternators, dynamos and control boards.

In some cases it may be desirable to use an additional screening cowl on alternators. Cable connections between generators and control boards must be kept as short as possible and associated engine wiring should be run separately by the shortest satisfactory route. Indiscriminate looping is bad practice. Current supply lines to electronic equipment must not be run near charging circuit wiring.

Sometimes the main shaft causes interference, and because the frequency changes with engine rev/min, control boards and generators are often blamed. The cure is to fit a phosphor bronze earthing brush running on the shaft.

Interference may also be generated by outside sources such as other craft, nearby workshops or any unscreened installations. This can easily be checked by simply shutting down all rotating electrical equipment on board and stopping the engines. If, then, the interference continues it is coming from some outside source.

All electronic equipment such as radar, radio-telephone, echo sounders and so on must be bonded through low-resistance conductors, such as tinned copper tape, to some common point. The main engine is suitable, or a free-standing batten above the level of bilge water, but not the inner side of the ship's planking.

Careful attention to screening and bonding and the use of correct materials and components will ensure adequate control of unwanted radio frequency interference.

PART IV

Electrolytic corrosion

Closely allied to the installation of electrical power and

equipment aboard a boat is the problem of electrolytic corrosion induced by leakage currents. Electro-chemical action causes nearly all underwater corrosion of metal and the subject is therefore of prime importance to owners and operators of marine craft.

The corrosion occurs when dissimilar metals are immersed in an electrolyte and connected electrically outside the electrolyte. The effect produced is galvanic and it can happen naturally as above, or be caused by leakage currents from electrical equipment on board.

Sea water is an excellent electrolyte and any metal immersed in such a saline solution has a voltage potential. If this potential is more than 0·25V between two such immersed metals which are in contact, electrolytic action will take place.

The process consists of current flow from the anode, the metal with the low potential, to the cathode, the metal with the high potential, and the loss in solution in the electrolyte of ions from the anode. This loss of ions is the corrosion affecting the anode.

Although the phenomenon is normally thought of as occurring when dissimilar metals are involved, the process can equally well apply to components made from identical metal as the result of local conditions such as pressure, heat stress, mill-scale and differences in paint surfaces which have changed the voltage potential of the immersed metal. For example, in a steel-hulled ship the rivets, because of the heat and stresses occurring during their formation, have a lower potential than the steel hull and so they act as anodes to the cathode of the hull and the galvanic effect takes place.

One of the basic laws of electricity is obeyed by electrolytic corrosion in that for every anode there is a complementary cathode and the path of least resistance between them is the one chosen. The severest corrosion takes place in situations where the anode is small in area and the cathode large. For example, while a painted surface gives protection, small imperfections such as pinholes and abrasions allow a multitude of minute galvanic cells to form where a potential difference exists between the

86

Page 87 : 13 (*above*) CAV spring-starter motor; 14 (*below*) Lucas M45 oil-and-water sealed starter motor

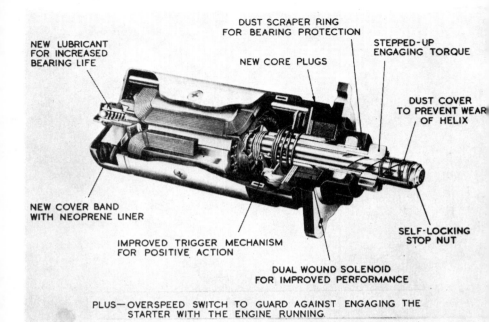

DUST SCRAPER RING
FOR BEARING PROTECTION

NEW LUBRICANT
FOR INCREASED
BEARING LIFE

NEW CORE PLUGS

STEPPED-UP
ENGAGING TORQUE

DUST COVER
TO PREVENT WEAR
OF HELIX

NEW COVER BAND
WITH NEOPRENE LINER

IMPROVED TRIGGER MECHANISM
FOR POSITIVE ACTION

DUAL WOUND SOLENOID
FOR IMPROVED PERFORMANCE

SELF-LOCKING
STOP NUT

PLUS—OVERSPEED SWITCH TO GUARD AGAINST ENGAGING THE
STARTER WITH THE ENGINE RUNNING.

Page 88: 15 (*above*) Cutaway drawing of the CAV CA45 co-axial starter motor; 16 (*below*) CAV 357 'Thermostat' cold-starting aid for diesel engines

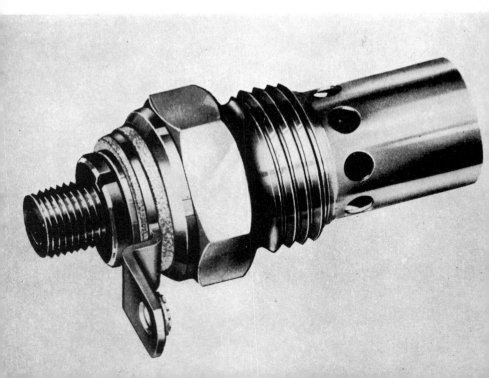

good and the damaged, or poor, painted surface. In such conditions corrosion attack is localised and intense.

In order to prevent the loss of metal from the anodic areas it is necessary to make them cathodic so that no corrosion takes place. To do this enough current must be applied through the water to drive the hull and former anodic sections cathodic.

One of two methods is used to achieve the desired protection— the impressed current or sacrificial anode. The first, the impressed current method, is primarily in use in ships which have available a constant supply of direct current, enough of which is passed through anodes of inert material to make the vessel the cathode of a galvanic cell. The advantage of this system is that the degree of protection may be controlled to suit changing conditions of water temperature and salinity and thus any transition from sea water to fresh water.

In the second method sacrificial anodes of low-potential material such as magnesium or zinc are used. Because of the low potential of these metals compared with other metals normally used in the construction of boats, they will always act as anodes to the hull and underwater fittings causing them to become cathodic. The advantages of this system for yachts and smaller working craft not normally described as ships are that no outside source of current is required and the only loss of metal is from the sacrificial anodes which are easily replaced when corroded away.

While the basic principles of cathodic protection are straightforward enough, application to individual craft is another matter. Every installation has to be specific to the particular boat and its normal environment of operation. It is essential to use the services of a qualified cathodic-protection engineer who will have the necessary specialised knowledge.

However, it is necessary to appreciate that even when a craft is cathodically protected there is still a risk because leakage currents from electrical equipment, if sufficiently strong to overcome the current flow of the protective system, can set up a galvanic cell, causing former cathodic states to become anodic, which will then result in the corrosion taking place. In other words any circumstances which result in a flow of current through the water from anode to cathode will result in this electro-chemical action.

It will by now be clear how important it is that the boat owner, when commissioning new building, or buying a new or second-hand craft, ensures that the electrical installation is carried out exactly in accordance with practices laid down by those qualified to do so, and to have the work supervised or checked by a suitably qualified person. The following summary of the recommendations of the Marine Division of CAV/Lucas will make the requirements clear.

The insulated return system should be used and to this end all CAV/Lucas marine alternators, dynamos and starter motors are insulated return types.

The earth return system suffers from the disadvantage that if the insulation of the insulated poles fails, leakage occurs and this can happen easily enough when, for example, junction boxes are located in damp or leaky positions, or if oil or water can get into starter motors or generators, or when deck sockets and exterior electrical fittings are badly installed or maintained.

Stray currents, particularly in earth-return systems, produced by insulation faults, cause stray currents which flow through the sea water between underwater fittings such as shafts, propellers and A brackets and result in loss of metal by electrolytic action. Such leakage currents can be of the order of 250–500mA at which corrosive attack is rapid and severe. When saturated a ship's inner planking can be an effective conductor for stray current. So also are wooden battery boxes and cases which have been affected by spillage of the electrolyte.

The risk of electrolytic attack should be taken seriously and any action to prevent it is well worthwhile. The following points summarise the requirements:

(i)   System to be of insulated return.

(ii) Provide and use an isolating switch in the main battery circuit.

(iii) Wiring should be insulated and sheathed, of at least 250V grade and of the correct duty rating.

(iv) Sockets, junction boxes, bilge detectors and similar fittings must all be protected against ingress of moisture.

(v) Avoid indiscriminate looping into one circuit, resulting in overloading and with consequent overheating and deterioration of insulation.

(vi) Cables should be fastened at regular intervals to avoid sagging and possible fracture.

(vii) Auxiliary equipment metal work must be earthed to a common point such as the main engine mass and no attachment should be made to the ship's planking.

In craft large enough to have an easily accessible engine room, earth lamps in series with the main bus-bars give early warning of leakage current and should be checked daily.

When ac equipment is operated on mains voltage in connection with shore-based equipment, the earthing of such equipment must always be back to the shore earth point, never to the ship's system. Ac battery chargers should be of the double-wound transformer type and they must be protected from damp and splashing.

It is now very unlikely that dc shore mains will be encountered, certainly in UK. Dc was at one time considered useful because ships' batteries could be charged from the mains by connecting them through a suitable resistance in series with the shore main. But this was both highly conducive to electrolytic action and dangerous because of the risk of personal contact with exposed conductors at mains potential.

While the introduction of electrical installations in boats calls for care and attention to detail, it is sufficient for the average boat owner to understand something of the basic factors. It is satisfactory enough if his knowledge is limited to that required for proper management and maintenance of the equipment. When it comes to design and installation the important thing is to know where to go for qualified information and advice. Unless the problem is of the simplest nature an initial approach to the equipment manufacturer's advisory service will ensure that reliable information is obtained. If contact is made with an electronic organisation or individual engineer assurance of competence in *marine* installations should be obtained before any work is commissioned.

CHAPTER 7

BATTERIES

The part played by the battery in a marine electrical installation is of far greater significance than is the case with the car. The management requirements, too, are more exacting because of the more severe operating conditions and the demands made upon it. While with luck the car battery gets an occasional top up and wipe over, a far less casual approach is needed in the marine sphere if efficiency and safety are to be maintained.

While the vehicle battery has primarily to supply current for engine starting and having achieved this is immediately put on charge, and secondarily to operate a few low wattage lamps when not being charged, the ship's battery is called upon to provide much greater service and may have to continue to do so without the benefit of recharging for considerable periods at a time.

For these reasons more care and attention must be given to allocation of duties, capacity and installation, than is necessary with the vehicle. There is also an alternative type of battery to be considered, whereas in vehicle applications the lead acid battery is used universally.

The basic function of a battery is to take in, store and supply electric current whenever it is required. To do this satisfactorily for as long a life as can be obtained from it requires that it shall not be too small for the job, that it shall never be totally discharged and that it shall operate in suitable environmental conditions.

The special relationship between battery and engine starting is

dealt with in Chapter 8. Management of batteries is just as important as is management of engines. In fact it may be considered
an integral part of engine operation, as is lubrication, fuelling
or cooling, for if the battery is not maintained in top condition
engine performance will suffer, perhaps vitally, when an
emergency start is called for.

Electric current always available at full power is also essential
for the proper functioning of the other electrical services aboard.
Failure of navigation lights or electronic navigation aids could
lead to a dangerous situation and inadequate current supply in
the domestic circuitry would lower the efficiency of appliances
and, in craft using refrigeration, result in deterioration of food.

Lowering of battery performance can happen for a number of
reasons and a routine of regular inspection and checking should
be established. It is all too easy to forget the battery and there
are not many boats regularly placed in the care of skilled hands
for servicing as is more often than not the case with the car.

What, then, is involved in good battery management? Let
us first consider the types of battery in use. For marine use there
are two types. Each performs the same function as a unit for
storing and providing electric current, each differs in construction
and materials and there are also differences in management
requirements. The types are the lead acid and the alkaline. Both
should be designed specifically for marine use such as the Lucas-
CAV lead acid ac range or the Alcad Nickel Cadmium marine
batteries, either of which will give longer and more reliable
service in marine installations, if properly looked after, than
those not so designed.

Each type has its own particular advantages which will be
looked at in a moment. Briefly, the lead acid is cheaper initially,
has a shorter working life, will self-discharge and will deteriorate
if left in a discharged state.

The alkaline, on the other hand, is a good deal more costly
initially, has a much longer working life, does not self-discharge
and can be left in a discharged state.

At first sight the alkaline seems to be much superior, but

when costs are offset against the lead acid the various factors more or less balance each other out. Both types may be used together in one installation provided certain precautions are taken, as will be explained. The lead acid battery is the type familiar enough in the automotive world. In fact car batteries can be perfectly suitable for marine use, but it is preferable to use the units known as 'heavy duty'. It does depend of course on the installation. In the small boat with low horsepower engine and Dynastart unit, the heavy duty battery is not essential. But in batteries, like in everything else, you get what you pay for and the cheap battery can never be recommended for use in a boat. Preference must be given to batteries produced by a known manufacturer and specified for marine use.

In the Lucas-CAV range of batteries the various types are classified as follows:

(1) Heavy duty—flat plate—normally used when for the heaviest starting duties.

(2) Heavy commercial—suitable for the medium range of starting loads.

(3) Light commercial—the type suitable for the small cabin cruiser.

(4) ac range—a range of batteries specially developed for use with alternators.

The capacities available are normally up to 300Ah in 6 and 12V units, but greater capacities are sold as individual units of 2V rating. These are used in larger vessels with separate battery compartments.

Lead-acid batteries must receive regular charging, whether they are used or not. This is one of the first requirements of good management, particularly in craft which are used infrequently, and during the time the battery is laid up ashore. This is because while standing idle they slowly lose charge and the rate of loss quickens with rise in temperature, so that the warmer the conditions in which they are stored, the more rapidly the discharged state is approached. At moderate temperatures of about 18 °C (65 °F) the loss is about 1 per cent/day. This increases to some 3 per cent/day at 38 °C (100 °F), which is quite a sharp rise in discharge rate.

Apart from this self-discharging phenomenon the lead-acid battery deteriorates appreciably if left in an uncharged state for long or is allowed to self-discharge without being charged for more than two or three months due to sulphation of the plates. It follows therefore that when circumstances are such that batteries are in irregular use, and when they are in storage, regular hydrometer readings should be taken to check their state of charge which is determined by measuring the specific gravity of the electrolyte. Average hydrometer readings at a temperature of 16 °C (60 °F) would be:

> Fully charged   1·280
> Half charged   1·200
> Fully discharged 1·115

The capacity of the lead-acid battery is related to its rate of discharge and is normally expressed in terms of a 10hr rating. For example: a 250Ah battery will, at the 10hr rate, supply 25A for 10hr. At a higher rate of discharge the capacity of the same battery will be reduced, only 60 per cent (150Ah) of the rated capacity being available at a 2hr rating.

Apart from hydrometer testing for measurement of the SG a high rate discharge tester is used to obtain an indication of a battery's condition. The prongs of the tester are applied to each 2V cell in turn. Good condition is indicated by a steady voltage being held for 10sec, but if the voltage falls rapidly the cell is weak. For these figures to be accurate the battery must be at least 70 per cent charged.

It is not sound practice to use a high-rate discharge tester when a battery is under charge because of the risk of a spark igniting the hydrogen which is emitted from the cells under this condition.

Normal charging should be at the 10hr rate but, if a battery is in good condition and its temperature is not allowed to rise beyond 43 °C (116 °F), higher rates may be used. It is important to check temperature carefully, particularly when batteries are on charge in unventilated engine rooms in which the ambient temperature may be high.

Charging rates can be calculated as follows:

$$\text{Rate} = \frac{C}{T} \times 1\cdot4$$

where C = battery capacity in ampere hours, T = charging time in hours, $1\cdot4$ = factor for battery efficiency (approx. 70 per cent).

Then, with a 250Ah, 24V battery:

$$\text{10hr rate} = \frac{250}{10} \times 1\cdot4 = 35\text{A}$$

or, with a 140Ah, 12V battery:

$$\text{10hr rate} = \frac{140}{10} \times 1\cdot4 = 19\cdot6\text{A}$$

These calculations show the theoretical basic charge rate. In practice, of course, the generator control board takes charge, permitting a high-charge rate at the beginning of charging and gradually reducing the rate as the battery voltage rises. As charging proceeds the specific gravity of the electrolyte will rise. It will have reached its maximum when no further increase takes place after three successive hourly readings. Then charging must stop.

The alkaline battery is made up of two or more cells crated together to give the capacity required. For marine purposes 5, 9 and 18 cells are used for 6, 12 and 24V systems respectively.

There are three types of alkaline marine batteries and it is important to use the type most suitable for the particular duty involved. These are:

(1) *Nickel-iron tubular*. This type is suitable for the larger craft where heavy duty with regular and continuous cycles of charge and discharge take place. They will not hold their charge for long periods as they are subject to open circuit losses.

(2) *Nickel cadmium flat plate high performance*. This type can deliver very heavy discharge currents and is particularly suitable for engine-starting duties. Fully charged it will hold its capacity for many months, self-discharge losses being extremely low.

(3) *Nickel cadmium flat plate normal resistance*. This is an excellent general purpose battery for the smaller craft. It is suitable for engine starting and general duties such as lighting and providing current for domestic appliances, but, as with all batteries, those used for engine starting should not be called upon to also provide current for other purposes. Again self-discharge losses are very low.

For normal resistance cells the discharge capacities for alkaline batteries are at a 5hr rate. For high-performance cells the rate is 2hr. To ascertain the charge rate a calculation of 0·2 of the total battery capacity for a 7hr period is made. A battery of 250Ah capacity would normally accept a charge rate of 50A for 7hr, that is, 0·2 of 250 = 50A.

It is quite safe to use higher charge rates provided the maximum cell temperature does not exceed 45 °C (113 °F).

The state of charge of an alkaline battery does not affect the specific gravity, but this will vary with temperature. A normal SG figure at 20 °C (68 °F) is 1·200, but as deterioration of the electrolyte takes place this will gradually fall. When this happens the electrolyte must be renewed and the manufacturer's advice should be sought. A high-rate discharge tester may also be used on alkaline batteries, but it must be specifically calibrated for a given battery size and type. Gassing must not be taken as a sign that an alkaline battery is fully charged.

The charge to discharge ratio is the same as for lead-acid batteries, 1·4, ie 140Ah charge is required to get the battery back to full capacity after a discharge of 100Ah.

To offset the much higher cost of alkalines as against lead acids, the alkalines do offer advantages which may make the financial outlay worthwhile. It largely depends on how the craft is used and an owner's particular requirements. It is not, for example, essential to remove the alkaline from the boat when laying up, provided it is at least 80 per cent charged, and there is no need for regular trickle charging throughout the winter. Also the electrolyte must be kept at the correct level and in the older type of steel cases there was only a shallow space for the electrolyte above the plates. In the up-to-date plastic cases in which the cells are now normally contained there is more room and it is easier to see and maintain the level.

Corrosion is not a serious risk with nickel cadmium cells which are supplied in either steel or polystyrene containers. The electrolyte, potassium hydroxide, is actually a preservative of steel. But if a steel crate is used to contain the cell units it must be painted or otherwise treated as a protection against corrosion.

The general management requirements are much the same for both types of batteries. Topping up to maintain the electrolyte level, keeping cell tops clean and dry to prevent leakage currents and corrosion, ensuring that overheating does not occur and, in the lead acid, avoiding total discharge, are the most important points.

Batteries should always be isolated when not in use and for this purpose an isolating switch, placed in an accessible position, must be installed. But a word of warning must be given when alternators are used. The isolating switch must never be used to open circuit a running alternator as the abrupt cut off creates high voltage surges which can immediately and irreparably damage an alternator's rectifying diodes.

Normally lead-acid and alkaline batteries should not be used together for the same application because a small amount of acid will damage alkaline cells beyond repair. If an installation includes both types, separate hydrometers, clearly marked for identification, are essential.

Lead acids and alkalines produce hydrogen during charging and so there is always a risk of explosion. Depending on the type and extent of the battery installation, therefore, precautions, such as those recommended by Lucas-CAV, should be taken:

(1) All connections must be kept clean and dry.

(2) Battery stowage spaces must be kept well ventilated by natural or mechanical means.

(3) Only fans of the gas or flameproof type should be installed in the outlet vent.

(4) Inlet air must be trunked to below the battery and the outlet be taken from the deckhead.

(5) Open areas must be provided, and maintained, over the top of the battery to prevent concentration of gases.

(6) Adequate size cables should be used to prevent over-heating and all connections must be well made.

(7) Any equipment which can cause arcing such as switches, relays or fuses must not be positioned in the battery space.

(8) When the battery installation is large ventilation fans should be run throughout the charging cycle.

(9) The installation must secure the batteries against the vessel's motion and should be provided with stowage trays.

(10) Lead-acid batteries require a lead-sheathed tray and alkalines a steel tray.

A good indication of the adequacy of battery management is given by the rate of consumption of distilled water (Fig 6).

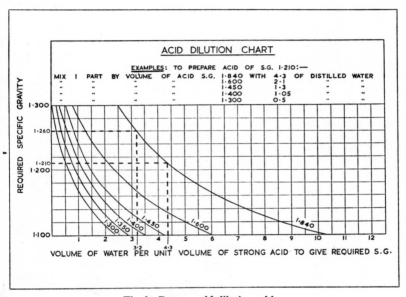

Fig 6   Battery acid dilution table

Too much used means overcharging, or overheating of the battery compartment, or both, while low water consumption implies under charging and the charge rate should be checked.

Dirt and corrosion usually accumulates around the terminals and this should be periodically removed and a check made to ensure that the batteries are fully secured in position. Proper battery fillers which help to prevent over filling are supplied by Lucas-CAV and Alkaline Batteries Ltd and are to be recommended.

Cable connectors are often fitted in an unnecessarily ham-fisted manner and this is quite wrong, being both potentially harmful to the battery and serving no useful purpose. They should be lightly tapped into position with a wooden instrument such as the handle of a screw driver. Never should they be hammered home and never, if there is a self-tapping screw, should this be used to tighten a connector. The screw is provided to ensure that a tight joint is maintained after the connector has been gently tapped into position.

In a multi-battery installation, and particularly when there are separate batteries for engine starting and the other electrical services, diode splitters may be used to control the flow of charging current from the generator. Their function is to direct the current to the battery which is the most run down and prevent a run-down battery taking current from one which is more fully charged. Lucas-CAV and Valradio Ltd are suppliers of diode splitters and technical and installation data may be obtained from them (Fig 7).

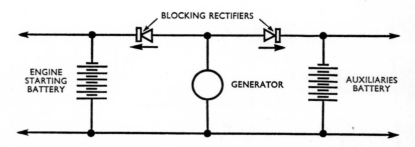

Fig 7   Circuit diagram showing blocking rectifiers for controlling the charging current from one generator to two sets of batteries

Batteries are not cheap, whichever type is used, and a great deal depends upon them. They are a vital part of the ship's mechanical installations and have a direct relationship to the vessel's safety. Adequate management and maintenance is therefore essential.

CHAPTER 8

ENGINE STARTING-SYSTEMS

In the matter of starting the modern marine engine is no less reliable than the car engine. The fuel mixture control is set according to whether it is a hot or cold start, the button pressed or key turned. Hardly anyone thinks twice about it. Gone are the days of the temperamental cumbersome beast of uncertain temperament.

Provided fuel in correct proportion enters the cylinders at the right time and there is full compression and a properly functioning means of ignition, then, if the engine is turned over at sufficient cranking speed, starting is a near certainty. Most power units require some form of starting drill, but this is quickly learnt, and if carried out on every start becomes automatic. There is the usual golden rule, of course. Follow the maker's instructions.

Before looking in detail at the more common types of starting-systems it is as well to understand some of the problems involved in starting an engine from cold, and hot, which latter condition sometimes requires a more precise drill or more care.

To give meaning to the condition of a cold engine we can use the comparison with the human athlete coming first to the track, whether to practise or race. His first requirement is to warm up. Until he has done so he is unable to run smoothly and at speed. Even if the weather is warm he is still cold in the athletic sense. His muscles are comparatively taut, joints stiff and blood circulation and temperature inadequate for smoothly efficient performance. So, not without quite an amount of disproportionate physical effort initially, he starts his limbering up. As he proceeds it all becomes easier. Less effort is required and he is soon feeling the freedom of movement and power of which he is capable—and an engine is the same. Mechanical parts, mechanisms, are cold and, compared with their condition at operating temperatures, reduced in size. The oil is sluggish, having a higher viscosity than at running temperature, causing drag between the moving components and giving a relatively poor separation of sliding metal to metal faces. Today's multigrade oils give much better starting than the older lubricants which relied to a much greater extent on their 'body' for effectiveness. Nonetheless, these oils need warming up, just as do the engine parts. Then there is the fuel, entering cold cylinders, cooling off, tending to condense, suffering uneven distribution and incomplete combustion. In the petrol engine, the fuel/air mixture finely vaporised and mixed by the carburettor, tends to return to globules of petrol separate from the air, giving such poor combustion that a specially rich mixture is needed. This extra petrol—much more than is required at running temperatures—dilutes the oil on the cylinder walls, partially destroying lubrication and giving risk of excessive wear. When the plug spark burning is erratic, some of the petrol escapes altogether and flows away through the exhaust system.

The diesel engine is a somewhat better proposition from the point of view of quick warm up because of its much higher compression. Also the fuel mixture does not have to pass through a cold induction system before entering the cylinders. It is therefore less prone to condensation and in a better and warmer condition when the fuel is squirted into it. Even so, diesels for operation in abnormally cold conditions are often provided with cold starting equipment such as the glow plug which provides an artificial hot spot in the combustion chamber. This device is somewhat like a spark plug, but with a filament instead of a spark gap which heats up to a required temperature when activated by current from the battery.

Both types of engine, however, suffer the same condition of

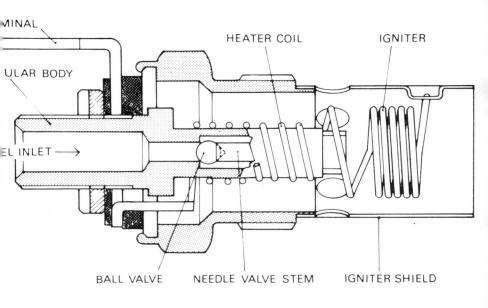

MINAL

ULAR BODY

EL INLET →

HEATER COIL

IGNITER

BALL VALVE   NEEDLE VALVE STEM   IGNITER SHIELD

Page 105: 17 (*above*) Diagram of CAV 'Thermostart'; 18 (*below*) sectional view of the CAV AC7 ventilated alternator

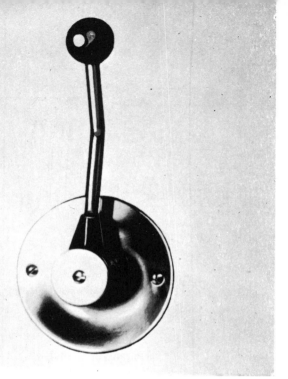

Page 106: 19 (left)
VETUS single
top-mounting
side lever control

20 (right) VETUS
twin top-mounting
lever control

cold working parts and sluggish oil and both need to be started and brought up to working temperature as quickly as possible. This applies to any type of modern fast-running engine in boat or car. The old practice of letting the motor run slowly to warm up would be harmful to the modern engine, preventing adequate lubrication and prolonging condensation.

Apart then from the actual methods and equipment used, what are the basic essentials for quick, reliable starting? Assuming the engine is in good working order, full compression on each cylinder, sparking plugs or fuel injectors working, valve and ignition timing correct, induction system gas tight, exhaust system clear of restricting deposits (particularly important in the case of the small petrol/oil two-stroke engine) and the engine is free to turn, that is disconnected from the propeller, the most important single factor is adequate cranking speed, for this means that the engine parts function positively and the starting system is not overloaded, which if allowed to happen will cause rapid deterioration of the human arm, the electric starter motor or whatever other device is used.

This can be easily appreciated by those who operate hand-start engines today or have had experience of earlier units which had fits of cussedness. When they were on form a quick pull up against compression, or winding them round like a sewing machine, had everything going with minimum effort. But on the temperamental occasions the arm quickly tired and any persistent cranking soon exposed the frailty of human strength reserves. Much the same thing happens with electric starting which, as will be seen, can be expensively affected by persistent slow cranking and sluggish starting.

Calculations of the approximate power required to bring a cold engine to life give some idea of the loadings involved. A petrol engine requires about $\frac{1}{100}$ part of its power and a diesel, because of the much higher compression, nearer $\frac{1}{30}$. These figures are not precise, but suffice to indicate the scale of effort required to overcome inertia.

Of the various methods of starting, the most common today

is undoubtedly the electric system followed next perhaps by hand cranking on the smaller engines. But even these are increasingly fitted for electric start, the starter motor often serving as a dynamo when the engine is running to deal with battery charging, and for small boats such a system is very effective allowing also for the operation of such essentials as navigation, compass and cabin lights. These further considerations have been dealt with more fully in Chapter 6 ('Electrical Installations'), and the reasons for deterioration of electric starter motors under persistent conditions of slow cranking will be discussed later. Other systems, which will also be examined, are less in evidence, which does not imply that they are less effective.

Even though electric starting is fast becoming normal even for small craft, there is nothing wrong with hand cranking except, perhaps, that it requires physical effort and in boating, no less than other activities, human exertion is considered to belong to a past era. But as a starting system, hand cranking is just as effective as electric, inertia, gas or any other method. Why? Because it provides the required action, rotating the crankshaft and setting the engine's mechanical parts in action so that fuel is drawn into the cylinders and fired.

It also has certain advantages. It is cheap. It requires no ancillary equipment adding to costs and maintenance. But perhaps its chief attribute is to bring the operator into a close relationship with the engine, providing a person sensitive to mechanical things with quite an insight into its whims and fancies, and engines do have these moods, being affected by atmospheric differences as, for example, dryness or humidity, heat or cold and variations in fuel.

Hand cranking can also be maddening, reducing the human being to a state of near insanity, with crippled back and useless arm. But when this happens the engine is the culprit, not hand cranking as a starting-system.

Apart from the mechanics there are certain essentials for efficient operation of hand starting. Primarily these are a matter of engine installation and layout. There must be room to operate, and room to get the body into a position where the necessary power can be applied without contortions which can only reduce effort and lead to strains and sprains. Sometimes it is very difficult in a small boat to find the necessary room. In that case the best that can be done is to work out a position and technique and then stick to it. To some extent the characteristics of the engine will determine the requirement. The type which starts best with a pull-up-and-over compression—half a revolution of the starting handle, usually best done upwards from bottom dead centre—will be easier to manage in a restricted space than will the one which likes to be turned over quickly like a sewing machine.

Whatever may be the conditions, never apply sudden effort with the body in an awkward position. Get balanced, get a steadying hold and take the strain slowly. This way maximum effort can be exerted without injury risk. All this is easier to say than do, particularly when the engine is wanted urgently in a seaway. But the human frame is immensely strong if the loadings are applied correctly and a starting technique learned and adjusted to the particular engine's requirements will prevent all sorts of disasters.

No such problems arise with electric starting, but again there are certain essentials if the system is to function properly and be reliable. Compared with the requirements for hand cranking, the problems of space to operate hardly exist, for the starter motor is small and, being permanently bolted to the engine flywheel casing, well out of the way.

But of all the electrical equipment on the boat it is the one which requires the most current and imposes the biggest drain on the battery. This requires that the engine should be a good starter, that the battery should be kept in good condition and that the power cables from battery to starter motor should be of adequate size and that all terminals and joints should be kept absolutely clean. In Chapter 6 these requirements were examined in greater detail.

In operating principle the starter motor is no different from any other electric motor. It has a revolving armature located on a central shaft, or spindle, which rotates inside fixed coils attached to the motor body. Current is fed to the armature windings via brushes and the commutator and the attraction and repulsion between magnetic fields set up by the energised coils causes the armature to rotate. There is no speed control. The motor draws from the battery the current it requires to turn the engine and it is automatically cut out as soon as the engine fires.

The connection between the starter and the engine is through two gear wheels—a toothed ring fitted around the flywheel perimeter and a small matching toothed pinion located on the starter-motor spindle. The ratio between these two is about 10:1, which means that the effort exerted by the motor is multiplied ten times.

There are two main methods of obtaining the necessary connection and disconnection between the pinion and the flywheel toothed ring. On engines up to moderate horse power the Bendix drive is used in which part of the starter-motor spindle is threaded, the thread being of the rather coarse pitch type somewhat like a wood screw. The toothed pinion is a loose fit on this thread and is free to move along it. When the shaft starts to turn the pinion initially resists movement because of its inertia and so is 'screwed' along the shaft until it engages with the teeth on the flywheel. Being then in effect locked to the starter shaft, it turns with it and so turns the flywheel. As soon as the engine fires the flywheel turns faster than the pinion— over runs the starter motor, in fact, because the gear ratio is reversed—which then disengages and moves back along the threaded portion of the shaft.

All this action is quite automatic, occurring every time current is fed to the starter motor by pushing the starter button or turning the ignition switch to the 'start' position, but as soon as the engine fires the switch must be released.

On larger engines involving higher starting loads, pre-engagement type starters are used, the prime object being to prevent premature ejection of the pinion from the flywheel.

In this system the pinion is moved into engagement with the flywheel ring electrically, before full current is supplied to the motor. Overload and overspeed protection is taken care of by a plate or roller clutch. Earlier pre-engagement motors were equipped with manual operation of the pinion through mechanical linkage controlled by the operator, but in current practice this has been superseded by electrical control and the whole action of the starter motor and engine starting is automatic.

There must be immediate disconnection when the engine fires as otherwise the flywheel would drive the starter motor and the excessive armature speeds would soon result in damage to the unit.

The high current used by the electric-starter motor requires a suitable heavy duty switch having substantial contacts. Such a switch would not be successful if designed for manual operation and so the duty of closing the contacts is undertaken by a solenoid, that is, a soft iron rod, or plunger, surrounded by a coil consisting of many turns of wire. When current flows through the coil it sets up a magnetism which moves the plunger which closes the contacts, and the heavy current then flows from the battery to the starter motor. The advantage of this system is that a light-duty ignition switch is suitable because the solenoid coil is energised by low current. High-current circuitry is thus kept right away from the engine control panel or console.

It might perhaps be mentioned that on old engines equipped with electric starting the solenoid was often attached to the starter motor and operated by a lever actuated by a wire cable led back to the control panel. To start the engine the ignition was switched on and the cable pulled by its knob until the engine fired. Such units may still be found today, particularly in elderly craft fitted with automotive engine conversions.

Generally speaking the Bendix drive is used for petrol engines, but diesels, with their higher compression ratios, require a somewhat tougher starting effort and the arrangement which places the pinion in contact with the flywheel ring first is favoured. While the mechanical lever method of doing this has been described, there are other arrangements. In the 'axial' starter the complete armature assembly and pinion moves forward axially to engage the pinion with the flywheel. In the co-axial starter the pinion and pinion sleeve travel along the armature shaft to engage the flywheel. Yet again there is the non-axial type in which the pinion moves forward slowly under controlled conditions to become gently, but fully engaged with the flywheel before full current is fed to the motor. Whatever the system all these sophisticated mechanical and electrical arrangements are operated automatically, it merely being necessary to press a button or turn a switch to bring them into operation.

Another electrical starting system developed specifically for small craft with engines of cubic capacity in the range of about 40cc to around 850cc, either petrol or diesel, is the 'Dynastart' made by Siba Electric Ltd. As can be gathered from the name, the unit consists of a dynamo and starter motor combined, but having the characteristics of a separate starter motor and generator.

In operation the unit first converts electrical energy to mechanical energy providing high torque for engine starting and operating exactly as a normal electric starter motor with Bendix type pinion engagement. Then, when the engine is running, converting mechanical energy to electrical energy by performing the function of a dynamo supplying current for battery charging.

Operation is by key switch or push button in the usual way and the unit is fitted with a reverse current or cut-out switch and would normally be used with a voltage regulator. Rotation can be either direction, clockwise or anticlockwise, and, for two-stroke engines not equipped with a mechanical reverse gear, reversible rotation operation is available.

The unit is mounted on the engine by means of a swing bracket which must be of sufficiently robust design to prevent any undue flexibility, and the drive is by a V belt from the engine flywheel direct or through suitable pulleys. It is not a difficult matter to fit a Dynastart unit to an existing hand-start engine. The manufacturers provide standard installation kits for a number of engines and will advise for other power units when necessary. Even a non-mechanical owner should be able to fit a Dynastart which mainly consists of bolting on the various fitments using existing engine studs and nuts as indicated in the installation instruction sheet. It is, however, essential to guard against overspeeding of the unit which should not be run at more than 10,000rev/min except for very short periods. This means careful selection of pulleys to ensure the correct ratio is used giving an acceptable balance between cranking and generating speeds. Although a high ratio seems desirable to give greater starting torque and lower engine speed for full charge current, high-speed running should always be avoided if possible. As an example, if the Dynastart produces 5A at 3,500 armature rev/min, a 2:1 ratio would give an engine speed of 1,750rev/min for that output. With a 3:1 ratio the same generator would produce 5A with an engine speed of only 1,666rev/min. In these two circumstances all would be well. But should the maximum engine speed be 3,600rev/min these two ratios would give Dynastart speeds of 7,200rev/min and 10,800rev/min and the latter would be considered too high for continuous running.

Also, while an engine has a maximum rated speed it is more than possible that this will at times be exceeded, either deliberately or accidentally, as, for instance, if the engine was knocked out of gear while running at cruising revs.

When an engine is fitted with a Dynastart as standard equipment it can be assumed that the correct pulleys have been fitted. Even so it is important to know what engine revs could overspeed it and there will probably be a warning about this in the handbook. If a secondhand boat with a Dynastart engine is bought and no engine handbook is available it is worth getting in touch with Siba for advice. Alternatively, if the engine operating revs are known, the ratios can be found by measuring the diameter of the pulleys, or flywheel and pulley.

On larger diesel engines starting is often by mechanical means. There are various systems such as compressed air fed direct to the cylinder from air bottles charged by an engine-driven compressor; cartridge starting which is a rather specialised system more likely to be found in industrial diesel engines; the inertia starter in which the energy built up in a fast-turning flywheel is harnessed to crank the engine, and the spring and hydraulic starters, both of which are suitable for medium-power engines.

The spring starter looks much like the normal electric starter motor and is fitted to the engine in the same way. It is, in fact, in most cases interchangeable with the electric unit. Its action, however, is mechanical and it eliminates the need for batteries, generators and heavy duty cables.

Apart from being very simple to operate even though it will start diesel engines of six cylinders each up to 1l in capacity, it offers additional advantages. Being dust and damp proof it is particularly suitable for marine use in all climates and conditions. But perhaps its most unique feature is the facility it offers of turning the engine over slowly through its own reduction gear when tappet adjustment, spill timing and fuel-system priming is required.

The working principle is simple enough. A winding handle is used to turn a mechanism which compresses a spring consisting of dished spring washers located on a common sleeve. The drive to the engine flywheel is the normal Bendix arrangement and as soon as the winding handle is turned the pinion engages with the flywheel teeth. Further winding of the handle, up to about twelve revolutions, compresses the springs, while the main shaft is held stationary. The starter is then fully charged and ready for use. To release the stored energy and start the engine a hand-operated trip lever is pulled and the main shaft rotates rapidly until the springs have returned to their normal uncompressed position. For starting a hot engine full compression of the springs is not necessary. When the engine fires and overruns the starter the pinion is thrown out of mesh in the normal way. The winding adaptor, to which the winding handle is fitted, can be varied in position in increments of $8\frac{1}{2}°$ so that the most convenient angle can be chosen. Loadings on the handle, which operates through a reduction gear, are not excessive and, although more physical effort is required than with electric starting, it is a starting system offering high output with ever-ready, virtually *

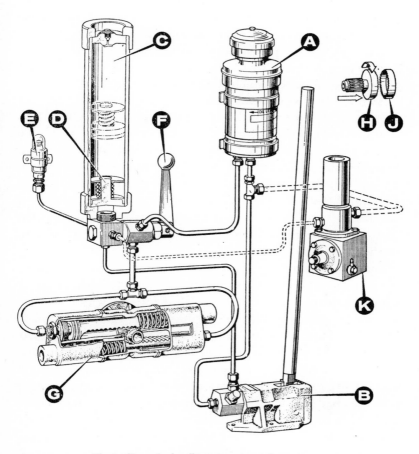

Fig 8   Bryce hydraulic starter-system layout

A	Feed Tank	F	Operating Lever
B	Hand Pump	G	Starter Unit
C	Hydraulic Accumulator	H	Pinion
D	Accumulator Piston	J	Engine Dog
E	Pressure Indicator	K	Automatic Charging Pump

cost-free operation under any conditions, requiring no ancillary equipment and only minimal maintenance.

Somewhat more involved, but similar in its lack of need for batteries, generators and cables, is the Bryce hydraulic starter in which highly compressed nitrogen contained in a sealed cylinder acts in conjunction with hydraulic fluid to operate a mechanical piston-rack, and provides the energy for engine starting (Fig 8).

The principal component is the hydraulic accumulator. This is a cylinder in which a simple free piston operates. The cylinder space above the piston contains the nitrogen compressed to about 2,800lb/in² and permanently sealed in. To provide energy for operating the starter unit hydraulic fluid is drawn from a feed tank by hand pump and pumped into the accumulator below the piston which unless activated by the fluid rests on the bottom of the cylinder. Continuation of the pumping forces the piston up the cylinder until the nitrogen is further compressed to 4,250lb/in². The piston is not subjected to strain by this operation and the system cannot be overcharged with fluid due to the protection of a relief valve. An indicator shows the pressure reached.

The other main component is the starter unit which consists of two opposed cylinders each containing a piston-rack engaging with a common pinion which in turn is integral with a toothed dog mating with a corresponding dog on the engine crankshaft end ('dog' is an engineering term used to denote a particular form of linkage between two mechanical components, in this case toothed wheels, or cogs). The pinion and racks have a helical tooth form which throws the pinion dog into engagement with the crankshaft dog in similar manner to that of the Bendix drive.

To operate the starter the starting lever is pulled until some resistance is felt, which is the point at which the pinion and crankshaft dogs engage. This initial resistance is overcome and the pull continued on the lever until it comes down to its stop. It is thus a two-stage operation which admits first a slow feed of pressurised fluid to the starter pistons to cause the gradual turning of the starter dog and then admitting full pressure to the heads of the piston-racks causing high-speed rotation of the crankshaft with a high starting torque. The pressurised fluid acting on the starter piston-racks comes of course from the accumulator unit motivated by the 4,250lb/in² pressure of the nitrogen.

After the engine starts, or at the end of the starting operation, the starting lever is released, the fluid returns to the feed tank and the piston again rests on the bottom of the accumulator cylinder and the system is set ready for re-use. The cycle can be repeated indefinitely.

Only minimum effort is required to build up the fluid pressure in the accumulator by the hand pump and recharging the system takes little more than a minute. A small automatic pump can be used instead of the manual effort if required. On large engines requiring a whole charge for each start a second accumulator can be installed, but smaller engines may get up to three starts from one charge. If the hand pump is operated with the accumulator uncharged and the starting lever in the open position, slow, precise rotation of the engine crankshaft is obtained, as in the case of the spring starter, for tappet and fuel supply adjustments. Remote starting control can be arranged and there are a number of combinations covering partial to fully automatic operation.

So much for the main starting-systems—hand cranking, electrical, spring and hydraulic—likely to be encountered in the sizes of craft covered by this book. There is one other type of mechanical starter device likely to be increasingly found on small engines up to 200/300cc, namely the recoil starter. This really comes under the heading of hand cranking, but could conveniently be used in situations which made turning a starting handle difficult or perhaps almost impossible. The recoil starter consists of a cord fitted with suitable moulded rubber handle, which winds up around a spring-loaded drum. When the cord is pulled a ratchet on the base of the drum engages with a slotted ring on the crankshaft end and the engine is turned over. When the engine starts, or when another pull is needed, the cord is released and automatically winds back on the drum, the ratchet then operating at the trail. The whole device is protected by a metal casing with flanges or feet to bolt down on the engine.

Sometimes, and in certain environments, diesel engines, with their high compression ratios, are difficult to start and a starting aid is used. Probably the best known of these is the CAV 'Thermostart' type 357 starting aid. This is a device mounted in the inlet manifold upstream from the first inlet port or manifold division. It is fed direct with diesel fuel from a separate vented container which is automatically topped up when the engine is running. The unit consists, basically, of a valve body, electric heater element and igniter coil. In action fuel flows to the valve body where it is heated and vaporised. When the engine is cranked and air is drawn into the manifold the vaporised fuel is drawn over the igniter and burns, thus heating the inlet air. Cold start procedure is to turn on the starting aid switch—which is spring loaded to 'off'—and keep the unit energised for 15–20sec. Then the engine starter is operated while still keeping the unit energised. Both switches are released when the engine starts, provided that does not take longer than about 10sec, in which case the cranking is stopped for a few seconds with the starting aid left energised. Cranking is then resumed and the sequence repeated if necessary until the engine starts.

The other device is made by the Plus Gas Co and is called the Plus Gas Super Start. It consists of an aerosol with a standard spray head containing highly flammable materials having a very low flash point, which form combustible mixtures with air over wide air/fuel mixture ratios. The device, which is not attached to the engine, but hand held, is suitable for use with all types of engines. In operation the spray is simply directed into the air intake and thus aspirated into the combustion chambers along with the inlet air. The makers suggest that some two to three hundred starts should be obtained from one can of the product.

CHAPTER 9

ENGINE COOLING-SYSTEMS

In simple terms an internal combustion engine is a heat machine. In order to function it must create heat until the different parts reach their proper operating temperatures. Once that stage is reached, however, it is necessary to control the heat produced or in a short time destructive overheating would occur.

While, as will be seen in Chapter 10, the lubricating oil plays a part in engine cooling, it would not in itself be sufficient. There must be a continual process of cooling all the time the engine is running and so some cooling medium has to be used. In conventional engines this is either air or water. Whichever it is, the same basic requirements apply. There must be a plentiful supply of it and once it has done its job it must be conducted away without delay. To meet these conditions engine designers adopt various systems and an important function of engine management is to ensure that the cooling-system is operating properly at all times.

It is sound practice to make a habit of systematic observation of instruments or other visual indications of engine operation. This is not difficult and soon becomes quite automatic. But it does provide an insurance against continuing to run an engine when something goes wrong, because, whatever the defect may be, if it does not actually stop the engine it is almost certain to cause a change in the operating temperature and this will show at once on the water temperature and cylinder head temperature gauges.

Many small engines of the type used in yachts and launches are not fitted with temperature gauges as standard, although these may be added by the owner. But the same principles apply and the routine checking will consist of regular glances over the side to see that the cooling water is still flowing at the right rate, and even developing a sixth sense, or subconscious awareness of the sound, temperature and 'presence' of the engine.

In larger craft the power units are installed and sound insulated in such a way that overheating or other malfunctioning could easily go unnoticed and so comprehensive instrumentation is provided. Even so, it will not take an owner with a feel for machinery long before he becomes so familiar with the working sounds of his engine that he will be immediately aware of any out-of-normal change. For non-mechanical owners it is no less important to know what is going on in the engine room and so he must train himself to the dial-checking method.

What, then, do the various engine cooling-systems consist of, how do they operate and what are the operator's responsibilities?

Air cooling is straightforward in principle, consisting of a continual provision of an adequate volume of cold air passing over the engine and being conducted away as hot air, at a flow rate sufficient to maintain the engine at correct operating temperature. In practice there are certain requirements which must be met and which make air cooling a little more difficult than it sounds.

The main problems are related to the provision of adequate air flow past the particular parts of the engine which get hottest, and conducting the heated air away quickly. A single-cylinder engine presents the least problems, but will serve to illustrate how the function of air cooling operates.

The parts which get hottest are in the region of the combustion chamber, cylinder head, exhaust valve and exhaust manifold. In these regions the engine designer provides increased metal to air surfaces in the form of fins and these will be larger than the fins in other parts of the engine. The reason for this is that when hot metal is exposed to a cooling medium, in this case air, the heat flows from the thickest to the thinnest parts. Thus the fins are tapered and made as large as possible in these areas so that the heat is dissipated as rapidly as possible.

Relying entirely on a flow of air for essential cooling, the air-cooled engine demands careful consideration in regard to installation for it is a fundamental of an efficient air-cooled operation to provide both an adequate supply of cold air and take away hot air as quickly and efficiently as possible. Therefore intelligent attention to ducting is essential. The engine manu-facturers usually provide alternative layouts of ducting to suit different types of craft, or they will advise when requested, and as usual their recommendations should be followed. Basically there must be an unrestricted flow of cold air from atmosphere to the engine and an equally unrestricted exit for the heated air to atmosphere. And this air movement must take place at a rate sufficient to ensure the desired engine cooling. In anything but the very smallest installations like, for example, certain little air-cooled engines used in launches, the air movement must be forced, by means of a fan.

There is a positive relationship between the areas of the inlet and exit ports, the internal dimensions and length of ducting and the capacity of the fan. If necessary this must be worked out with the engine manufacturer. Also important is the positioning of the inlet and outlet ports, which must always be unobstructed and, in the case of the outlets, facing aft for preference where they will not be affected by beam winds which could in certain conditions interfere with the outflow.

Another important consideration covers the positioning of the inlet and outlet ducts. It must never be possible for the inlet and outlet air streams to mix. In cases where the cylinder is exposed to atmosphere for cold air, the heated or exhaust air must be carried away in ducting. This is, of course, no more than commonsense because, unlike a motorcycle air-cooled engine which requires no ducting due to the speed at which it is moved through the air, an inboard marine engine is, in this sense, relatively stationary and so the heated air must be collected and conveyed away under controlled conditions, both for maximum cooling efficiency and for safety and comfort aboard.

The cold air ducting may be reinforced flexible plastic piping. For fabricating shaftings metal or glass-reinforced plastic (GRP) are suitable materials. Hot air ducts should be made in metal suitably lagged with plastic asbestos or something similar and if, as is quite common practice, the engine exhaust piping is combined with it, the effective ducting outlet must be of adequate area and this should be checked with the engine manufacturer.

The hot-engine cooling air exhaust may also be used for domestic heating, being ducted to interior accommodation, oilskin lockers and storage cupboards and providing, through causing air movement in the ship, a desirable means of ventilation, before being ducted away to atmosphere. In all, the air-cooled engine, which is available in a number of makes in useful horse power ranges, offers certain attractions, such as the elimination of hull skin fittings, pipes, pumps and water jackets—and a form of central heating if desired.

However, it must be admitted that water-cooled engines far outnumber air-cooled units and the systems in use involve rather more complications. They can also be affected by exterior conditions and so involve the operator in, at times, the necessity for remedial action, such as clearing weed-choked inlet filters, freeing jammed pumps or, as sometimes happens in small engines, dissipating air locks.

Basically there are two water cooling systems in use, the direct and indirect. The direct system takes sea water (or, to use the more usual technical term, raw water) in from beneath the boat, conveys it through piping to the engine water jackets and exhausts it through more piping out through the side or transom back to sea. It is a system favoured in craft intended to operate in fresh water which does not cause corrosion in water jackets, but it has also been in use for very many years in smaller units operating at sea.

The indirect system employs closed circuit fresh water to cool the engine and raw water to cool the fresh water. This

Page 123:
21 (right) The Lister
SW2MGR water-
cooled diesel engine
developing 15bhp
at 2,000rev/min

22 (left) Watermota
Shrimp propulsion
unit with petrol/
paraffin engine,
shafting and variable
pitch propeller
complete in
ready-to-glass-in
GRP tray

23 (right) The
Brit 'Sprite'
10hp four-stroke
petrol engine

Page 124: 24 (*above*) The Perkins T4.108 turbocharged four-cylinder
diesel engine developing 65shp at 3,800rev/min; 25 (*below*) the Watermota 'Sea Wolf' 10·30hp four-cylinder petrol engine

method eliminates the danger of corrosion of engine parts by sea water and has the added advantage of being free from possible contamination or blocking by weed and other extraneous matter (Fig 9).

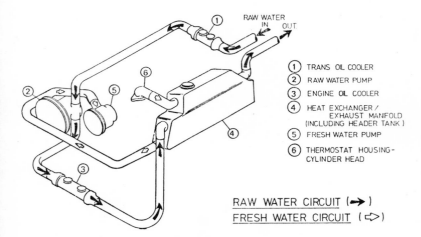

1 TRANS OIL COOLER
2 RAW WATER PUMP
3 ENGINE OIL COOLER
4 HEAT EXCHANGER / EXHAUST MANIFOLD (INCLUDING HEADER TANK)
5 FRESH WATER PUMP
6 THERMOSTAT HOUSING - CYLINDER HEAD

RAW WATER CIRCUIT (➤)
FRESH WATER CIRCUIT (⇨)

Fig 9 A typical fresh- and raw-water cooling system

Alternative cooling arrangements are by radiator or by conducting the fresh water through pipes running alongside the keel or otherwise beneath the boat. A radiator may only be used successfully if it can be supplied with a continuous flow of cold air and have the heated air conducted away quickly. In most installations these requirements would call for properly designed ducting and in all probability a fan to provide the air flow. In the keel or other forms of underwater piping, the closed circuit water is cooled by flowing through the portions of the pipes which are continually immersed in cold raw water.

The most usual practice is to employ a heat exchanger which, being located on the engine, allows for the simplest, and therefore most economical, installation. The heat exchanger is in effect a bundle of tubes through which the fresh water passes after circulating through the engine. Cold raw water is circulated around the pipes, so cooling them and the fresh water within them, and is then exhausted overboard.

Pumps are used in both circuits to ensure a flow of water at the required rate, these being driven by the engine. Both centrifugal pumps with impellers, and plunger type pumps, are used, normally in fresh- and raw-water systems respectively. Invariably such pumps are self-priming (Fig 10).

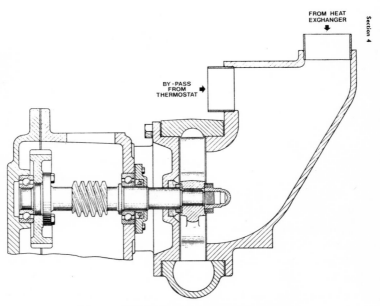

Fig 10   A fresh-water pump and drive detail

A typical centrifugal pump consists of a metal housing containing waterways and an impeller located on a drive shaft. The impeller is a disc fitted with a number of vanes which when rotated force water outwards by centrifugal force, causing it to flow under pressure into the water jacket and so through the engine's waterways. There is a seal on the drive shaft to prevent water running along it. Impellers are now usually made of neoprene and should not be run dry, but it is highly unlikely that priming will be necessary. Nevertheless, the engine handbook should be checked for any special instructions in this respect.

The fresh-water system usually incorporates a thermostat, the purpose of which is to cut off the flow of water to the heat exchanger when the engine is cold, thus allowing the impeller to circulate water only within the engine, resulting in rapid warm up. Once the correct operating temperature is reached the thermostat opens the circuit to the heat exchanger and the full cooling-system is brought into action.

Thermostats are of two types, both operated by the water according to its temperature. In one type a thin metal bellows containing a volatile fluid is connected to and actuates the thermostat valve. When the water is cold the bellows are collapsed and the valve is shut. As the water heats up the volatile fluid expands, enlarging the bellows by concertina action and causing the valve to open. Water then flows to the heat exchanger.

The same principle applies to the other type of thermostat, but in this the concertina bellows are replaced by a wax element consisting of a rubber diaphragm encased in wax and containing a thin rod. The wax, sealed inside a brass container which is surrounded by the water, is affected by the water temperature. When it is cold the wax is thick and at minimum volume, and in this condition it holds the valve closed. When the water heats up the wax melts and expands, allowing the valve to open.

In a system using a header tank a pressure cap is used if there is no venting. This contains a main, spring-loaded valve, which controls the boiling point of the water, and a secondary spring-loaded valve which can allow the passage of air or water from the tank and an overflow pipe is connected to the pressure cap. Different pounds per square inch settings, controlled by the pressure cap, are used according to the engine manufacturer's specification. A replacement cap of the correct rating must be used. If the rating were too high, water-jacket temperature and pressure in the system could become excessive.

Antifreeze may be used in fresh-water systems. It is in fact essential in keel cooling if all the water cannot be drained off. The engine handbook will give recommendations on grade of antifreeze and quantities for different operating conditions. A normal mixture for use in Britain is between 25 per cent and 33 per cent content of the water. Modern antifreeze contains an additive giving protection against corrosion and it is not essential to drain the system at the end of each winter. Every two years is probably a reasonable period for draining, flushing out and replenishing with fresh solution.

The action of antifreeze is simple. It is usually an ethylene glycol compound which lowers the freezing point of water.

While an engine cooling-system is very much a matter for the engine manufacturer, there being little the owner can do about it, other than understand how it works and ensure that it is working, the ancillary equipment such as sea cocks, strainers, pipes and outlets are matters over which he has more control.

The sea cock permits and controls entry of raw water. It is fitted below the waterline in an accessible position. This is important for two reasons. First it must be easy to get at to turn on and off, it being good practice to make sure it is shut whenever the boat is left unattended, and, secondly, it must be possible to remove, clean and replace the strainer while the engine is running. It is customary to fit an inlet scoop over the sea cock inlet hole on the underside of the hull and this will prevent entry of large weed or other sizeable contaminating material. But the grill obviously cannot be too fine or the water flow would be restricted. All manner of water-borne particles and fine weeds may therefore enter the sea cock and be carried as far as the strainer which is of fine enough mesh to prevent their further passage. In bad conditions the strainer can become truly clogged causing a reduction in water flow with consequent lowering of the efficiency of the cooling system. If this happens the sea cock has to be closed while the strainer is extracted and cleared, and, provided the engine is not badly overheating, this can be done in such a short time that it is unnecessary to stop it. But it will be seen that the sea cock must be positioned where it can be got at quickly and in reasonable comfort. These components are made of manganese bronze or gun metal and standardisation gives ready interchangeability. Outlets are suitable for plastic-hose or copper-pipe connections.

Other skin fittings required in the cooling system are of course the water-exhaust outlets. These again are suitable for plastic or copper piping. The positioning of the outlet is important. In an inboard engine installation it should always discharge the exhaust water above the waterline.

For water piping there can be no doubting the desirability of copper. The increasing use of plastic hose cannot be regarded with favour until, if ever, a more suitable type of plastic, or a different specification material, is discovered. Of course it is less costly to install, requiring no special joints, but this seems to be about the only factor in its favour. It is potentially dangerous because it is easily damaged or destroyed by heat, or by a blow. A plastic pipe coming into contact with a piece of hot metal, for example, can be punctured in a few seconds. It is simply melted away and the hot object does not have to be red hot. The arguments in favour of plastic are, apart from the saving in cost, that if the piping installation is properly carried out the risk of damage is negligible and the chances of something hot enough to melt the plastic material getting into the engine compartment are so remote as to be not worth counting. This may be so, but plastic piping is a risk material and as such has no place on a boat, where safety is always of prime importance.

The recommended material for water piping is copper, annealed and preferably fitted with solderless union connections. There are sound reasons for these recommendations. Copper is not adversely affected by sea water or heat and is resistant to abrasion. When annealed it may be bent and manipulated, within all normal requirements, without risk of fracture. Furthermore, annealed copper is resistant to fatigue failure due to vibration. And it is for the same reason that solderless unions should be used, as solder can be fractured by vibration.

Vibration can be reduced by inserting short lengths of flexible piping to connect the engine to the water-piping system. If this is done the recommended material for the flexible piping is reinforced rubber hose. Alternatively, direct copper pipe to engine connections may be made provided a 'hairpin' bend is incorporated.

The·thing to remember is that however smoothly an engine may seem to run there is always some degree of movement and vibration. There is also movement of the hull, in the form of vibration directly related to the movement of the engine. Then again, the hull is, as we have already seen, affected by the water in which it floats, the varying loads it has to carry and the differences of alignment when the craft is in and out of the water. It is easy to see, therefore, that to attempt to make a rigid piping connection between sea cock and engine and engine and outlet is asking for trouble.

A further point related to the raw-water intake is the position of the inlet scoop. The important point here is that the system must be able to get water continually, whatever the degree of pitching and rolling. So it must be placed near the keel and as close amidships as practicable, depending on the type of craft and position of the power unit. In multi-engined craft each engine will normally have its own water cooling-system.

Whatever type of cooling-system is used—air, raw water or raw water/fresh water—its correct functioning is a vital part of the successful management of a marine engine. Correct operating temperatures mean efficiency, fuel economy and long unit life.

CHAPTER 10

ENGINE EXHAUST-SYSTEMS

The products of combustion emitted by an internal combustion engine are noisy, odorous, hot and lethal. They must be properly controlled without reducing the efficiency of the engine, burning the boat or deafening or killing those on board, all of which present certain problems. The aims are to install a system which does not impose a back pressure on the engine, but does ensure maximum silence and low-temperature operation, while at the same time being absolutely leak proof so that there is no risk of exhaust fumes entering or accumulating in any part of the craft.

Exhaust systems fall into four general categories, as follows:

(1) Wet exhaust with engine installed above the water-line

(2) Wet exhaust with engine below the waterline

(3) Dry exhaust with engine above the waterline

(4) Dry exhaust with engine below the waterline.

There are variations on the above depending on the type of boat, engine installation and layout and any engine manufacturer's particular stipulations.

The principles of each of the four general systems are simple enough to understand. The problems are usually associated with the physical aspects of installation.

The wet exhaust with engine above the waterline uses an exhaust pipe from the exhaust manifold running downwards to connect with the silencer which is located below the waterline. From the silencer runs a tailpipe which rises above the waterline in the form of an inverted U bend, or swan neck, before exiting above the waterline by means of a skin fitting. Water from the engine cooling-system is introduced into the exhaust pipe before the silencer, control being by a two-way cock, located at or near the engine water outlet, which gives either water to the exhaust or water overboard.

The wet exhaust with engine below the waterline does not use a two-way cock. Water is piped direct to the exhaust pipe entering on the exit side of an inverted U bend formed above the waterline. From this bend the pipe connects to the silencer which is again situated above the waterline, as is the tailpipe for its total length to the exit skin fitting. In craft intended to operate at sea or waters subject to wave formation, a fullway valve is fitted to the tailpipe just inboard of the exit position. This prevents sea water, which may enter the tailpipe, from flowing back to the silencer.

In the dry or wet exhaust with engine above the waterline the exhaust pipe, silencer and tailpipe may be used without a U bend, provided it runs down from the engine exhaust manifold, but above the waterline. With the wet system water is piped in before the silencer.

The dry exhaust with engine below the waterline allows for either piping from the exhaust manifold through an inverted U bend to silencer and tailpipe above the waterline, or down piping to silencer below the waterline with tailpipe up to a U bend and exit above the waterline. A fullway valve is always fitted in sea-going craft when the tailpipe is a straight run back to the silencer.

The exhaust manifold, piping and silencer are very much the concern of the engine manufacturer for they necessarily cause back pressure which has a restrictive effect on the flow of gases. The designer is faced with some problems in this matter because, while he must quieten the exhaust, he must not restrict gas flow too greatly or engine efficiency will be reduced. Something of the difficulties involved can be appreciated when it is realised that after combustion of the fuel in the cylinders the waste gases expand with very great force and enter the exhaust system under extremely high pressure at supersonic speeds. As each cylinder exhausts the gases form a shock wave in the exhaust manifold and in multicylinder engines these shock waves occur many thousands of times a minute. The shock waves slow down as they enter the exhaust pipe and by the time they exit from the silencer have expanded to become about the same pressure as the outside air. In the process most of the noise has also been reduced.

Pressure reduction and silencing is naturally essential. Most people will have heard racing engines running without silencing systems. Such noise would be totally unacceptable in normal circumstances and must be contained. But because of the design considerations it is unwise to alter an exhaust system or fit a different silencer without first consulting the engine manufacturer.

The wet exhaust system is usually recommended whenever possible with a water-injection-type silencer installed above the waterline. The alternative, as mentioned in the examples above, in which water is injected into the exhaust pipe, are equally satisfactory, but it must not be possible for water to get back into the engine and the two-way cock should be used so that just before the engine is stopped the water can be directed overboard, so that in the last few moments of operation the exhaust system dries out.

In marine use silencers should be of steel galvanised inside and out, brass, cast iron or synthetic rubber and it must be possible to drain and vent the water-injected type. There is a minimum size recommendation for the drain plug which should not be smaller than ¼BSP, that is British Standard Pipe thread. Dry silencers should either be water jacketed or lagged with asbestos yarn not less than ¼in thick, but for air-cooled engines this should be increased to ¾in.

There are certain limitations on the type of silencers used on diesel engines because of particular corrosive characteristics of the diesel fuel. For engines with wet-exhaust system brass and copper are not suitable and on dry exhaust absorption-type silencers should not be used. The synthetic rubber type of silencer may only be used with wet exhausts.

Silencers must be sufficiently robust to withstand internal explosion and they must, of course, be leak proof. This is particularly important in the type fitted with detachable ends for the purpose of cleaning.

Pipe lines should have as few connections as possible and be firmly supported, but the method of fixing must allow for expansion. Pipes should never be kinked, have sharp bends, or be pinched, and the installation should be carefully planned to avoid any area where there could be inflammable vapour, or where the heat from unlagged piping could scorch timber. If the system is not self-draining a drain cock should be fitted at the lowest point.

The outlet point is normally at a point 6in above the loaded waterline and, as mentioned, the termination is through a skin fitting. Sometimes a drowned outlet is employed, but this is a matter for the engine manufacturer to specify.

Piping may be iron, galvanised steel, copper or brass for wet or dry petrol engine systems, but never copper or brass for diesel, for which the only metals suitable are iron or galvanised steel, wet or dry. Synthetic rubber and asbestos pipes are only suitable for wet systems and then, for preference, rubber should only be used between the silencer and the hull, not between the silencer and the engine.

Flexible metallic exhaust piping, which is necessary at some point between engine and silencer for flexibility mounted engines, is suitable for wet or dry systems, but should not be installed in wet systems in such a position that water can lodge within them when the engine is not running.

Pipes should have unions or flanges at each end so that they can be taken out of the system when required without having to dismantle hull and engine fittings. The type of fittings, minimum bore and maximum length of pipes have a direct effect on engine performance and must be as recommended by the engine manufacturer.

To ensure an acceptable standard of noise reduction marine silencing-systems should be designed to meet an agreed maximum noise emission level of 85phons, with a permitted 10phons tolerance, the phon being the unit used in physics for measurement of noise. Measurement is made by a phonometer with the microphone 82ft from the engine, which must be run at maximum power at a speed specified by the manufacturer, and 4·1ft above the waterline. Four separate measurements are taken, from positions forward, to port, to starboard and aft of the engine.

Regular inspection of the whole exhaust system is essential. Subjected to changing temperatures, corrosive elements in exhaust gases, atmosphere, the moisture of condensation and the fatiguing effects of vibration, the pipes and silencers are probably more vulnerable to failure than any other components in a marine power installation. Exhaust gases leaking into the boat may be undetected and can be lethal. Carbon monoxide, for example, has no smell, but is poisonous. Defects often start as fine fractures, or pinholes, and flanges and joints are also points to watch.

CHAPTER II

ENGINE LUBRICATION

Metal surfaces moving in close relationship to each other, such as bearings and pistons and cylinders, must be lubricated or they will rapidly overheat through friction and fuse together, resulting in seizure.

Oil is the lubricant used to prevent this happening by maintaining a film between the moving metal surfaces at all times when the engine is running and also effectively covering all exposed interior metal surfaces when the engine is stationary to guard against corrosion from salt-laden air and moisture. What are the characteristics and qualities oil needs to fulfil these requirements?

First it must be tough enough in body to withstand the pressures exerted by the metal surfaces and thus maintain its film between them, even at high operating temperatures. Then, at the same time it must flow easily when cold when the engine is started up, because any sluggishness at this stage could result in metal-to-metal contact and rapid wear. It must also be sufficiently tenacious that when the engine is stopped it does not drain away entirely from all the metal surfaces, but leaves a thin film all over them. These in themselves seem formidable enough requirements and years ago if an oil did all this the engineer was happy enough with it. But today many more duties have been loaded onto the lubricant and to meet these modern technology has produced additives which now make oil one of the most versatile products, largely responsible for the long, trouble-free running of automobile and marine engines which have made breakdowns and frequent servicing annoyances of the past. What else does engine oil have to do?

It must, of course, lubricate. That is cut down friction and wear, the film between the metal surfaces forming a barrier on which they slide easily. It must also help to seal off hot high pressure gases and take away heat from hot areas, carrying it to the sump or to an oil cooler. It must reduce corrosion caused by the products of combustion and absorb and disperse harmful waste products. It must help to keep the engine 'clean' by preventing partially burnt, sooty, tarry deposits which escape past the piston rings into the sump and if not absorbed by the oil would form deposits in piston ring grooves, filters and oilways, causing rings to seize and obstructing the flow of oil. To achieve this the oil must carry these materials in suspension and so dispersants and detergents are added. These additives also help prevent the deposits coagulating into sludge. Another additive makes the oil slightly alkaline to deal with corrosion caused by acids formed when the fuel is burnt in the cylinders. At running temperatures such acids are in gaseous form but when the engine is cold they condense and it is then that they are neutralised by the oil.

The dispersants, the detergents and the anti-acid additives all play an important part in giving modern oils their remarkable ability to keep an engine clean. Not many years ago regular decarbonising was essential if an engine was to be maintained in proper trim. Now, all that has changed. The laborious, and (today) costly, decoke, if not actually no longer necessary, is required only very infrequently. If the engine is running well, giving its full performance without trouble or hesitation, it is as well to leave it alone, however many hours it has done. A good deal depends on how conscientious the operator is in following the engine manufacturer's recommendations on grades of fuel, types of oil, starting-up procedures and normal operating conditions such as maintaining cruising speeds at the correct rev/min.

Not the least of these recommendations will detail the frequency of oil changes and these are of definite importance in keeping an engine clean and in good shape. The reason is that the oil contains only relatively small quantities of the dispersant and detergent additives and they are relatively soon used up. This is particularly so if the engine is used on frequent short runs entailing cold stop-start conditions. When normal operations keep an engine running at working temperature for longer periods the oil additives are used more slowly. Nevertheless, their effective life is limited and so oil changing at makers' recommended periods, or even less if cold starts are frequent, is a rewarding if somewhat tiresome chore.

There would be little to be gained by going into technical details of the additives, but the oil property, or characteristic, which it is important to understand is viscosity, or 'thickness'.

This quality is identified by the familiar SAE number which represents the American Society of Automotive Engineers viscosity standards. The numbers 20, 30, 40 and 50 refer to an oil's viscosity limits at 99 °C (210 °F) and 5W, 10W and 20W indicate viscosities at −18 °C (0 °F). Only viscosity is indicated by the numbers, no reference being made to any other properties the oil may or may not have. For guidance it may be taken that the lower the SAE number the thinner is the oil. Today, of course, we have oils with viscosity characteristics related to both plain and W numbers, in other words, multigrades. The reasons for this development will become clear if we examine how the viscosity of an oil affects its performance within the engine.

The two main requirements from an oil are, as we have seen, to separate moving parts and act as a seal against hot gases at high pressure. If it is to successfully separate the parts and yet enable them to slide easily in relation to each other, the oil must not be too thick, or it will cause drag, even though it will act successfully as a seal. Again thick oil causes cold starting difficulties by making the engine difficult to turn.

If, on the other hand, the oil is too thin it will fail as a lubricant, allowing overheating and rapid wear. It must therefore be thick enough to do the job, but not more so than necessary and this thickness, or viscosity, should as far as possible stay the same throughout the whole operating temperature range of the engine, from cold to hot and have also some reserve against possible occasional overheating.

As oil technology has developed so it has become possible to meet, to a considerable extent, the engine manufacturer's demands and, with multigrade oils, provide lubricants that remain thin to give easy starting from cold and yet still give good lubricating qualities at high operating temperatures. Typical SAE numbers for multigrades are the familiar 10W/30 and 20W/50.

It is important that an engine should be provided with oil of the right viscosity for its range of temperature variations and the engine maker's recommended grades (SAE ratings) of oils should always be used. Today all normal purpose automotive and marine engine oils are mineral based and there is probably very little to choose between any of the branded makes. There is nothing to be gained by saving a few pence buying oils of unknown or doubtful origin, any more than there is in listening to people who, having never bothered to keep up with progress in modern techniques of lubrication, will claim that detergent oils should never be used in two-strokes, or even in marine engines at all. It is surprising how many people there still are who, having not the haziest idea what an oil is required to do, will hold forth on the subject with convincing authority. Their advice is dangerous and should be ignored. In any case a modern marine engine uses so little oil that it can be no financial hardship to insist on using a manufacturer's recommended grade.

So much for the composition and performance requirements. What happens to the oil inside the engine?

When first put into the engine through the filler orifice the oil finds its way into the sump, which serves two purposes. One to hold the correct quantity of oil and the other to provide a relatively large surface area for dissipation of heat when, with the engine running, the oil returning to the sump is hot.

From the sump the oil passes through feed holes, grooves and drilled passages to the main bearings and through the crankshaft to the big end bearings, and in some engines also to the gudgeon pins. Subsidiary passages, usually known as bleeds or galleries, are provided for the oil to reach the camshaft- and rocker-shaft bearings. Other passages supply oil to timing gears or chain and maybe the chain tensioner. In all these arrangements oil is supplied to engine parts under pressure (Fig 11).

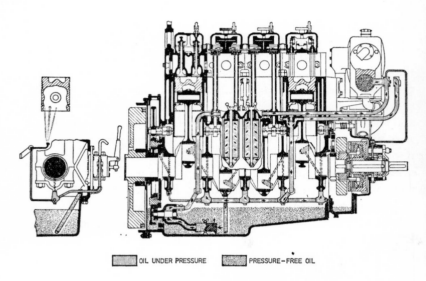

OIL UNDER PRESSURE   PRESSURE—FREE OIL

Fig 11   A typical engine lubrication system

The pressure is provided by a pump (Fig 12) which draws oil from the sump and circulates it at the rate of several gal/min through the oilways. The actual pressure is determined by the engine designer and controlled by a pressure-relief valve. In order to operate successfully a pump must work against a resistance. If that resistance is lacking it cannot create the necessary pressure. A simple example will explain this. Imagine a length of pipe, open at one end, with a pump at the other. If oil (or any other liquid) is introduced to the pump it will pump it along the pipe and out of the open end—at minimum pressure. The pressure could be increased by an out-of-proportion

Page 141: 26 (*above*) The Mercedes-Benz OM636 42hp four-cylinder diesel engine; 27 (*below*) the 80bhp model 4/254 marine diesel engine by G-Power Marine, a typical fishing-boat engine

Page 142: 28 (*above*) The Ford 250bhp turbocharged six-cylinder Turbo-Plus diesel as marinised by Sabre Marine Ltd; 29 (*below*) cut-away drawing of the Ford Turbo-Plus diesel, (inset top left) the turbocharger, (inset lower left) cooled oil jets directed at underside of the pistons, (top right) the intercooler

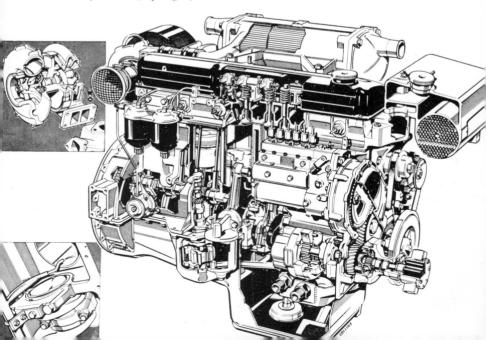

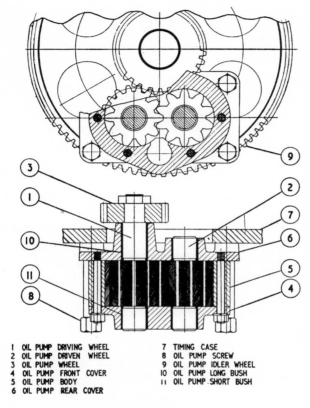

1	OIL PUMP DRIVING WHEEL	7	TIMING CASE
2	OIL PUMP DRIVEN WHEEL	8	OIL PUMP SCREW
3	OIL PUMP WHEEL	9	OIL PUMP IDLER WHEEL
4	OIL PUMP FRONT COVER	10	OIL PUMP LONG BUSH
5	OIL PUMP BODY	11	OIL PUMP SHORT BUSH
6	OIL PUMP REAR COVER		

Fig 12   Engine lubricating oil pump

step up in pump capacity or, more practically, by blocking up the open end of the pipe and drilling one or more small diameter outlet holes. Then the pump has something to work against in forcing the oil out through the holes and the column of oil in the pipe is under constant pressure. We can regulate the pressure by altering the size of the holes or the capacity or rate of operation of the pump.

This explains how it is that a new engine, with tightly fitting, unworn parts, has full oil pressure, whereas an old one with worn bearings does not maintain its oil pressure because the parts are loose fitting and so offer reduced resistance to the pump. In a partially worn engine which shows signs of falling oil pressure it is often the practice to change to a thicker oil which, having more 'body' to it, can compensate to some extent for the increased clearances and so lengthen the time to major overhaul.

Adequate oil pressure is a vital factor in the life of an engine because without it there would be a breakdown or loss of oil film between the metal parts which, however carefully and with whatever precision they may have been machined, have some degree of roughness which, in section seen under a high degree of magnification, look somewhat like irregular, jagged saw teeth. This roughness is always present in new engines and careful running in is needed to bed the parts reasonably smoothly together, which is why it is so important to treat a new engine gently for the first few hours of its life. During this initial running quite an appreciable amount of metal is rubbed off and the oil must, in addition to its prime function of keeping the surfaces apart, carry away this metal and dissipate the greater heat. The oil thus becomes heavily charged with metal particles during the first few hours of engine operation and it is also more affected at this stage by corrosive and contaminating gases and acids which are not present in such quantities in normal operational conditions. It is therefore particularly important to carry out the maker's recommended initial and early oil changes.

It may seem something of a contradiction to talk about a film of oil separating two moving metal parts which at the same time rub the high spots off each other. In fact it is the molecules of oil which maintain the barrier between the (relatively) flat moving parts. It is only during the running-in period, when the machined surfaces have ridges, or peaks, coarse or sharp enough to push through the oil barrier, that this happens. Once the rough surfaces have been honed down during the first few running hours, normal separation is maintained.

Running in a marine engine is not quite such an exacting business as it is with a car, because the operating speeds are lower and more consistent. Probably the most important thing is not to let the engine 'sweat' by causing it to take sudden loadings, particularly at low speeds. Actual revving under light or, if applied with care, normal loadings will not cause high wear and overheating in the early stages. There is no harm in letting the engine 'run free'. Applying heavy loadings at low revs is much more damaging. An understanding of what is happening in a new engine, common sense handling and oil changes at the right times are the best ways of ensuring long engine life.

Before considering pumps and filters it is worth examining the action of oil in lubricating bearings because while the pressures involved are often fully appreciated, it is sometimes difficult to visualise just how the oil film can be maintained between bearing surfaces and a shaft.

The phenomenon is made possible by the fact that the oil takes up the shape of a wedge, the action of which, as engine speed increases, becomes more and more powerful, so much so that the bearing surfaces are forced apart. The wedge forms because a shaft is always a clearance fit in a bearing. If it were not the fit would be so tight that it could not turn. There is, therefore, always a clearance of a few thousandths of an inch, say 0·0003in in a 2in diameter bearing.

The oil, fed under pressure to the bearing, forms a thin film where the clearance is greatest, that is on the side of the shaft opposite to the main pressure point. As the shaft rotates the oil is drawn round to the high load point and the wedge is formed. Fig 11 should make this clear.

The oil pump is a mechanical device driven from the camshaft or the crankshaft. There are two basic types, the gear type and the rotor type. Both operate on the same principle, drawing oil from the sump and forcing it through the engine oilways and eventually back into the sump.

The gear-type pump has two broad-toothed meshing gear wheels revolving in a closely fitting casing. Oil is fed in, drawn round the gears by the teeth and ejected to the oilways where, as already discussed, it meets with resistance. The gears nevertheless continue to turn and force more oil out of the pump and so the required pressure is achieved.

The rotor-type pump takes oil from the sump and forces it out to the engine in the same way, but the action is somewhat different in that there is an inner rotor meshing internally with an outer rotor which has an extra lobe. The two rotors revolve on different centres causing the oil spaces between them to vary in size and this creates the required movement of the oil.

As far as the boat owner is concerned, the type of pump is not of particular importance, but it is useful to have a basic understanding of how it operates.

The action of the pump is naturally very powerful and when oil is cold and does not flow easily through small bearing clearances, very high pressures could be built up which could damage the pump. The pressure relief valve is designed to prevent this by leaking oil back to the sump if a present maximum pressure is reached.

Oil is subjected to another form of pressure in the way of blow-by gases from the cylinders. These gases escape past the pistons into the crankcase and to provide for their removal crankcase breathers are provided. These are simply vents and in modern engines the gases are conducted back to the combustion chamber and burnt.

Every effort is made to keep engine oil clean. A strainer in the sump, known as the sump filter, collects the larger particles of metal and dirt which always accumulate and are carried in the oil. Then a full flow filter is fitted adjacent to the pump and, again, a bypass valve is incorporated to allow oil to flow outside of the filter if it is very cold and thick, or if the filter is so choked with sludge that oil cannot pass through it.

The external filter has a removable element in the form of a cartridge, usually made of resin-impregnated paper. It is very important that this should be regularly changed in accordance with the engine manufacturer's recommendations. If this is not done it will eventually become so clogged up that the bypass valve will operate continually and the oil will then circulate unfiltered.

The actual cartridge takes the form of a circular element folded into a number of shallow Vs. It fits between outer and inner casings, each having perforated holes. As the oil flows through the cartridge, metal and dirt deposits are lodged on it. It is worth remembering, when carrying out an oil change, that the external filter normally contains quite a quantity of oil, so that if the cartridge is renewed that much more oil will be required when refilling. The handbook usually mentions this.

There is another type of oil filter working on the centrifugal principle that dirt, metal and other solid matter is usually heavier than oil and so, in a circular container turning at high speed, such particles will be flung to the outside and held in the bowl, while the oil flows on through central ducting. This type of filter is not so common ~~as the gear or rotor~~ types. AS CARTRIDGE TYPES

Engine oil tends to be forgotten or neglected and often care is not taken over providing the correct grade. This is foolish, for probably no other single factor has such a direct bearing on satisfactory operation and long engine life as has its oil.

CHAPTER 12

PROPULSION AND
TRANSMISSION SYSTEMS

While closely linked in operation the propulsion and transmission systems do have quite distinct functions, each with its own part to play in harnessing and controlling engine power and converting it to motion of the vessel through the water.

By propulsion system is usually meant the propeller in one or other of its many forms, or a jet system, whereas transmission is related to gear boxes or direct drive linkage between the engine final drive shaft and the propulsion unit with the incorporation of operator controls.

Propellers and propeller shaftings are discussed fully in Chapter 13. Here it is sufficient to mention certain variations on the standard form of propeller. Probably the best known of these is the Hotchkiss Internal Cone propeller which, as its name implies, is fitted inside the craft rather than outside. The system has been developed by Donald V. Hotchkiss, a naval architect, over many years, and is today very widely used, having been brought to a high degree of efficiency and reliability.

Basically the unit consists of impellers which rotate within conical casings, hence the description cone propeller. The cone is in fact a centrifugal pump through which water is taken in from ahead and discharged astern with increased velocity, thus producing a reactive thrust.

The unit is installed in the bottom of the craft, by its flanges, and when positioned the underside of the cone is open to the sea. The impeller rotating in the large end of the cone draws water in from the small, or low pressure, end and causes it to flow spirally. This happens for about two-thirds of the length of the aperture and the water is then discharged tangentially from the other third. The final discharge flow is in force and thus drives the vessel. The design is self-cleansing. Grids prevent weeds reaching the cones in large masses by having the effect of preconditioning the weeds before feeding them to the cones in a controlled manner when they are ejected by the impeller.

The cone propeller system provides an internal form of propulsion and there are many advantages resulting from it. It allows the design of very shallow draft vessels which is desirable from the operational and seaworthiness point of view. Also, with the propellers placed amidships racing in a seaway is virtually eliminated. In an auxiliary powered sailing craft the system eliminates propeller drag when under sail.

There are many possible variations of the applications of cone propellers. By means of such devices as blanking off plates and piping and sea cocks, the discharge flow can be directed in any direction horizontally, giving ahead, astern or sideways thrust, variable at will, and piped water under pressure can be provided for uses in ship management, such as deck washing, trimming tanks and fire hosing. Bilge pumping, too, is a simple matter for the cone propeller.

Compared with standard propeller systems cone propeller revolutions are low and so a reduction gear is always fitted which means that high-speed engines may be used.

The Hotchkiss Cone Propeller is available in standard units covering craft from about 18ft up to some 250ft in length.

Harnessing the forces of reaction for boat propulsion has occupied the minds of designers and marine engineers for many years as, accepting the relative inefficiencies and minimal draft requirements of the standard propeller, they have tried to get greater thrust for available power, or cope with demands for very shallow draft craft to meet specific operational duties. Not surprisingly, therefore, the principles of the jet reaction systems have been studied in depth and with the high degrees of engineering skills and materials available today, considerable successes have been achieved.

The principle of the jet, whether it be of air or water, is straightforward enough, being in accordance with Newton's Law that every action has an equal and opposite reaction. In detail of engineering and function there is more complication involving flow patterns, nozzle design and the mechanics of a particular unit.

The system functions through the creation of a powerful jet of water directed to air, or into the water. Some idea of the power potential involved may be got from watching the effort required by firemen struggling to hold a high-pressure hose. The jet is produced by taking water in from beneath the craft, feeding it to a pump and ejecting it through a suitably designed outlet. The reactive force of the jet is limited to the maximum speed at which water can be forced through the system. This does not mean that the speed of the craft through the water will necessarily equal the speed of the jet. As will be seen in the chapter on propellers different hull forms are capable of different performances, but while a jet stream, unlike the conventional propeller, is not affected by the water in which the boat operates, the boat is, and so performance depends on several factors, including the capacity of the pump, engine power, the type of jet (discharge to air or to sea) and the hull form. In a displacement craft (speed formula: square root of waterline length in feet times 1·5 equals speed in knots) the same principle applies as with standard drive, ie once the maximum hull speed has been reached, more power will create greater wash and a related progressive reduction in extra speed.

A well-known example of the ejection above water principle is the SAIFJET marketed by Shippelle Ltd of Haslemere in Surrey. This consists of a single-stage axial flow water pump contained in a housing assembly which is bolted on to the transom, through which the drive shaft is taken for linkage to the engine. When the craft is at rest the impeller is partially submerged so that it may be primed for starting, but in action the SAIFJET discharge does not push against anything, except on going astern when the discharge is under water. There is one simple control for ahead, astern, reverse and neutral and the unit is suitable for transom-type craft up to about 25ft in length.

A water-jet unit designed specifically for installation in resin-glass boats is the UA HIGH POWER 6 marketed by UA Engineering Ltd of Sheffield. One of a line of water jets manufactured by the company, this model has the intake moulded in GRP which enables the unit to be glassed in to a GRP hull. It is suitable for engines up to 35hp in planing boats and up to 25hp in displacement hulls. A feature of the unit is its compactness, the length from the transom being only 11in and the height 8in. Two impeller sizes are available, 10in absorbing up to 15hp at 5,000rev/min and 14in absorbing up to 35hp at 5,300rev/min. Steering is by deflection of the jet from side to side or backwards under the boat. The movement is obtained from the action of two bucket deflectors pivoting on the tail pipe. Side to side control is by steering wheel or tiller, forward and reverse by a slide rod. Morse or Teleflex controls may be used if required.

Another, more sophisticated reaction unit is the Castoldi HYDROJET which is the result of Idrogetti Castoldi's research. It is marketed in UK by Norris Auto Products Ltd of Haywards Heath, Sussex. Employing its own transmission gears, rudder and jet deflector controls, the unit takes in water from beneath the vessel, accelerates the flow by impeller and venturi effect in the ducting and sprays it out at high velocity from the nozzle. An interesting feature is the jet deflector which, in conjunction with the movable nozzle, allows the jet to go directly aft giving forward propulsion, vertically downwards giving neutral, or ahead and downwards giving astern. A pressure-vacuum gauge is supplied as standard, but a full control panel is an option, as is a heat exchanger. The panel includes steering wheel, electronic rev/min counter, fuel gauge, switches, warning lights and ignition key. The horse power range is up to approximately 200.

Marine jet units covering a wide range of horse powers are supplied by the New Zealand firm of C.W.F. Hamilton & Co Ltd whose UK operations are conducted from Seer Green in

Buckinghamshire. Known as the COLORADA EXPLORER marine jet they are supplied in three versions, namely, single stage for 30–100bhp, two stage for 100–175bhp and three stage for 175–250bhp. The stages refer to the number of impellers in the system.

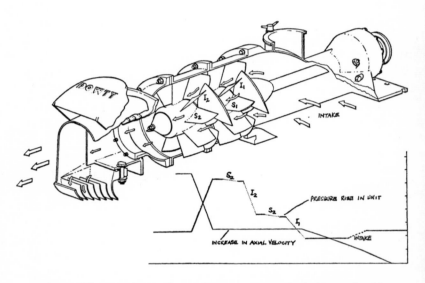

Fig 13   Diagram of water flow and pressure pattern in the Dowty jet drive

A prominent water jet unit giving high thrust is made by Dowty Hydraulic Units Ltd of Cheltenham, Gloucestershire (Fig 13). Four basic models are supplied in two jet diameters. These are: 12in single stage, up to 100bhp; 12in double stage, up to 200bhp; 16in single stage, up to 300bhp; and 16in double stage, up to 500bhp.

In these units the water jet is totally enclosed, a strong safety measure, and they are suitable for a very wide range of craft including lifeboats, working craft, runabouts and yachts.

Materials used in the construction of marine water-jet units are anti-corrosive and where necessary sacrificial anodes are provided by the suppliers.

Two possible disadvantages are relatively poor performance at low speed and the dimensional projection of the unit behind the transom which can make an appreciable increase in the overall length of the craft and perhaps make manoeuvring in restricted waters more difficult.

Against these factors there are the advantages of shallow draft, no underwater protruberances, weed decimation, variable direction of thrust, high static thrust and low underwater noise.

A system of conveying engine power to propeller which has

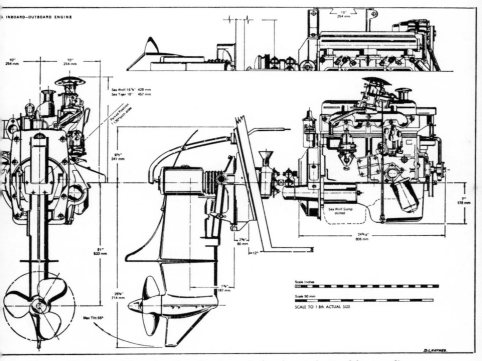

Fig 14   Watermota inboard-outboard power unit showing engine-to-drive coupling and transom mount

come into prominence in recent years, particularly for motor cruiser yachts, is the inboard/outboard configuration (Fig 14). In suitable applications this can combine the best of two worlds, allowing the designer much greater freedom in positioning the inboard engine by eliminating need for a fixed stern gear installation with permanently located propeller requiring the vessel to be operated in a certain minimum depth of water. At the same time the system permits the advantages of the outboard engine not the least of which is the ability to raise the propeller to or above the waterline when required. There is a range of these outdrives on the market, two well-known names being Enfield 'Z-Drive' and Volvo.

The Enfield 'Z-Drive' is suitable for diesel engine power inputs up to 75 bhp at 4,500 rev/min and petrol engine inputs up to 130 bhp at 5,000 rev/min. Both are available with power trim/tilt. The unit is transom mounted and installation is so simple and straightforward that it is claimed to be well within the capabilities of 'the average do-it-yourself enthusiast'. A standard mounting plate is provided for a transom raked at 12° to the vertical, with an adaptor block for transoms at other angles.

Engine power is taken through a flexible rubber-metal coupling to the drive-unit input shaft. Two constant velocity universal joints then transmit power to the top bevel gears and thence via the floating mainshaft to the gearshift bevels on the propeller shaft. Standard propeller rotation is anti-clockwise, ie looking forward when in forward gear, but rotation can be handed to give contra-rotation when twin units are used. Gear positions, controlled by an external lever, giving forward, neutral tnd reverse, are activated by an internal linkage to a sliding dog clutch on the propeller shaft. In reverse an automatic lock prevents the unit kicking up. A single-lever control cable and quick release cable fittings are used. Steering is by tiller arm or any standard wire rope or push–pull system.

The unit can be swivelled athwartships to port or starboard to a position 135° from the vertical for parking above water, or trailing, and there is also provision for a rearward lift up to 55° if an underwater obstruction is encountered. The power-operated trim/tilt unit, with single remote lever control and driveshaft for remotely mounted engines, is available as an optional extra.

The Volvo Penta outdrive units AQUAMATIC 100 and 270 accommodate horse powers of 115 and 130 respectively, being normally supplied as integral units to the Volvo Penta four-stroke OHV petrol engines AQ115A and AQ130C. Both units incorporate the Volvo 'Silent Shift' patented cone clutch. Electro-hydraulic lift is available and due to the design of the gears between engine and propeller the units are very quiet when running. Standard equipment includes instrument panel with electric revolution counter, electric temperature gauge and warning lamps for charging and oil pressure. Installation is facilitated by the collection of all electric cables into a single harness between engine and panel, the standard pack giving up to about 5ft between.

In the higher power range Volvo produce the Outboard Drive Model 750, a sophisticated unit with hydraulically operated steering and tilt and vibration-free rubber transom mounting. The tilt angle is 80°, which makes propeller cleaning or changing easy, and there are variable tilt positions to give trim control. A unique feature is the angle of rake which, bringing the propeller as near as possible to the transom, makes for accurate steering at all speeds. A large fin protects the propeller and further protection is given by the inclusion of a safety valve in the hydraulic system which allows the drive to tilt if an underwater obstruction is met. Forward, reverse and neutral drive positions are selected with the reverse gear unit which is fitted on the engine flywheel housing. The angle gears in the drive have helically cut teeth for quiet operation and the gears and bearings in the drive unit are designed for continuous maximum output in either direction of rotation.

A stern drive offering a different approach to the engineering requirements of these units is the TRANSA-DRIVE marketed by

Transa-Drive Distributors Ltd of Market Drayton, Salop. With a diesel rating of 85/90bhp at 3,500rev/min and 130bhp at 5,000rev/min for petrol engines, these drives have their gear boxes on the top rather than the bottom, an arrangement offering advantages that the size and shape of the housing is not limited and the under water pod, containing only a simple bevel drive, has a good underwater shape. The drive is through two angular constant velocity joints connected by a short splined shaft feed straight into the gear box cluster which consists of two bevel gears running on their own bearings around the input shaft and connected to a smaller horizontal bevel. A selector fork, with a dog form on both sides, is splined to the input shaft. These dog forms correspond to a similar form on each vertical bevel so that when the selector form is moved towards either of them the dogs engage to rotate the horizontal bevel on top of the drive shaft. The drive is then taken up by bevel gears to the propeller. The units can be wound up sideways to port or starboard through 120° with facility for locking in any position simply by removing the winding handle. Power tilt/trim is available as an alternative to the sideways lift facility, 50° of movement being provided. Propeller rotation can be either right or left hand and the steering is made to accept any push–pull system, the range of movement being up to 30° port and starboard. Minimal friction losses in the drive unit is ensured by the use of straight cut bevel gears mounted on their own ball bearings.

Yet another design approach to the outdrive system, this time to accommodate the output of larger diesel power units, has been made by the Saab-Scania Automotive Group of Sweden, an organisation well known for their Scania range of marine diesel engines. Having found no outdrive units available capable of absorbing power in the 250/300hp bracket, the Scania engineers developed their own system and in this they had the co-operation of the Swedish Navy. The aims were to produce a drive system with controllable pitch propeller, eliminating the need for a relatively bulky and costly reverse gear, to build in long working life and simplicity in design and maintenance. The result of these efforts was the HYDROP (the name derives from: *H*ydraulic *D*iesel *R*eversible *O*utboard *P*ropeller), a unit with a number of quite unique features.

It was soon found on trials that in this power category transom mounting was insufficiently secure. Therefore fitment was by flanging direct to the engine with free passage through the transom, which also reduces noise and vibration in the boat. Then the normal methods of suspending such drive units were discarded and a ball joint at the upper suspension point, and a Teflon bushing at the lower, were used, allowing the unit to rotate freely in all directions. Capping these two innovations was a hydraulic control system and a spring-loaded shift to reverse giving a fast action independent of hydraulic pressure.

The advantages claimed for the system include, in addition to the suitability for use with high-power diesel engines, the tractor propeller with hydraulically controllable pitch, eliminating reverse gears, allowing adjustment to any type of boat and to varying boat loads, an important factor for passenger-carrying craft, direct flange attachment to the engine with no load on the transom, 180° swing up travel to port and starboard, provision for single- or dual-lever control and a specially designed break-away device with progressive control of the resultant backward motion.

The HYDROP was designed by Saab-Scania primarily for use with Scania diesel engines to form a complete power-drive unit.

A transmission system requiring no mechanical linkage between engine and propeller is the HYDROMARIN Hydraulic Drive, a Swedish unit marketed in UK by G & M Power Plant Co Ltd of Ipswich. Consisting of a pump and hydraulic motor plus propeller shaft and stern tube the drive is operated by oil, fed under pressure through flexible lines to the hydraulic motor which is coupled direct to the stainless steel propeller shaft. A control valve in the circuit gives forward, neutral and reverse selection. Speed is controlled by the engine throttle. The drive unit is suitable for use with engines of wide horse power range and offers the considerable advantage that, because the engine to propeller coupling is by flexible hoses only, the engine can be placed virtually anywhere in the boat. Fixed shafting, with allied alignment problems, is eliminated and the propeller may be placed in its best operational position.

A propulsion unit introduced to the UK market in 1972 by Watermota Ltd, of Newton Abbot, Devon, is the SHRIMP. Consisting of an air-cooled four-stroke petrol/paraffin engine, control box, propeller shaft and variable pitch propeller, the unit comes complete with air-trunking adaptor, recoil starter, ½gal tank, stainless steel flexible exhaust pipe, exhaust skin fitting, propeller tube, grease gun, stern tube assembly or P bracket and shaft log. If required a GRP tray is supplied which enables the unit to be glassed in to a resinglass boat without the need for engine bearers.

Although the engine is small in the sense of horse power the unit gives high output in terms of torque, namely some 18·8ft lbf at 650rev/min continuous. This figure is so high that Watermota designed a special propeller for the unit of 12in diameter and 37in^2 of blade area. The result is that speeds of 4 to 6 knots are easily obtained dependent on the hull form at an average fuel consumption of 1½ pints of ordinary domestic paraffin/hour. Starting is on petrol with change over to paraffin per two-way cock. The control unit is lever actuated and, through altering the pitch angle of the propeller blades, gives ahead, neutral and astern. Installation requirements with no shaft alignment necessary are minimal and this unit appears to have much in its favour for launches and auxiliary sailing craft.

Before turning to the more conventional forms of transmission mention should be made of another system of propulsion which had some following in the 1930s, but would probably have disappeared by now had it not been for the development of an entirely new form of transportation, namely, the hovercraft, or aircushion vehicle. It is of course the airscrew or aircraft-type of propeller.

While not particularly suitable for marine use for obvious reasons, the airscrew does offer certain plusses. Stern gear installa-

Page 159: 30 (*above*) Cutaway drawing of a Ford marine diesel of the 2,400 range with cylinders inclined at $22\frac{1}{2}°$, toothed belt drive for camshaft, fuel and injection pumps and clover leaf depressions in piston crowns; 31 (*below*) the Dorman 6QTM diesel engine developing 285shp at 1,500rev/min with reversing reduction gearbox

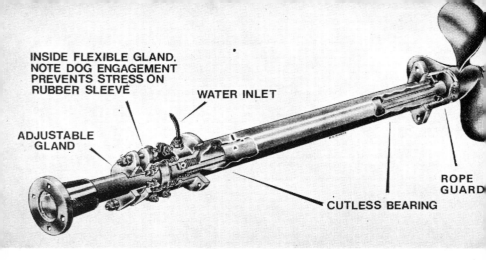

INSIDE FLEXIBLE GLAND.
NOTE DOG ENGAGEMENT
PREVENTS STRESS ON
RUBBER SLEEVE

WATER INLET

ADJUSTABLE
GLAND

ROPE
GUARD

CUTLESS BEARING

The Ralstan Modular Stern Gear is designed to simplify the task of yacht designers and boatyards. Throughout the range, dimensions will be held as a standard and all dimensions are given on the illustrations. The range is in three groups:

Group 1 1in diameter shafting only

Group 2 Metric stern gear 22mm, 25mm, 30mm, 32mm

Group 3 Shaft sizes, 1⅛in, 1¼in, 1⅜in, 1½in, 1⅝in, 1¾in, 2in

Page 160: 32 (*above*) The Ralstan Modular Stern Gear; 33 (*below*) the Kelvin T series diesel engine TA SC8 which develops 500shp at 1,350 rev/min

KELVIN

tion, shaft alignment and underwater propeller are eliminated enabling exceptionally shallow draft and direct drive from the engine to be used if required. Alternatively the engine may be

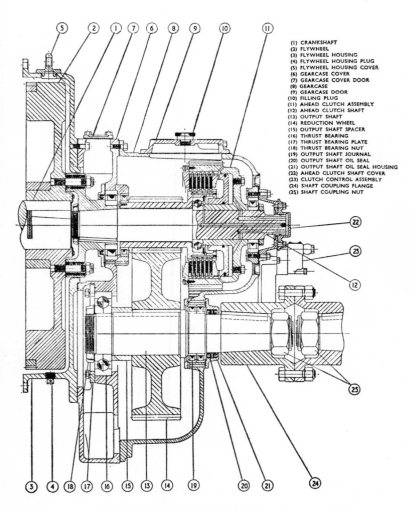

(1) CRANKSHAFT
(2) FLYWHEEL
(3) FLYWHEEL HOUSING
(4) FLYWHEEL HOUSING PLUG
(5) FLYWHEEL HOUSING COVER
(6) GEARCASE COVER
(7) GEARCASE COVER DOOR
(8) GEARCASE
(9) GEARCASE DOOR
(10) FILLING PLUG
(11) AHEAD CLUTCH ASSEMBLY
(12) AHEAD CLUTCH SHAFT
(13) OUTPUT SHAFT
(14) REDUCTION WHEEL
(15) OUTPUT SHAFT SPACER
(16) THRUST BEARING
(17) THRUST BEARING PLATE
(18) THRUST BEARING NUT
(19) OUTPUT SHAFT JOURNAL
(20) OUTPUT SHAFT OIL SEAL
(21) OUTPUT SHAFT OIL SEAL HOUSING
(22) AHEAD CLUTCH SHAFT COVER
(23) CLUTCH CONTROL ASSEMBLY
(24) SHAFT COUPLING FLANGE
(25) SHAFT COUPLING NUT

Fig 15   Marine gearbox, vertical section

positioned low in the boat which is good in relation to stability, in which case the airscrew may be driven by belt or chain.

On the other hand an airscrew is dangerous and must be protected by a heavy gauge wire cage which puts weight in the wrong place, and it is very noisy, which is inevitable because of the speed at which the blades move through the air.

The conventional form of transmission linkage between engine and propeller is the gear box which provides the operator with control over the direction of rotation of the propeller and enables him to stop it turning when necessary. There are many types of gear box and a number of different means of operating and controlling them. From the boat user's point of view there is little he can do in the way of maintenance and adjustment beyond keeping the oil level up to the correct place. Properly used a gear box will function indefinitely with very little attention. Any necessary maintenance will be detailed in the appropriate operating manual (Fig 15).

Not all gear boxes incorporate a reverse gear. In small-craft applications the functions required are no more than selection of neutral and engagement of forward drive, with the necessary reduction ratio. But with the increasing trend towards the use of relatively high-speed engines for propeller-driven craft a reduction ratio between engine-drive shaft and propeller is essential and for such application the gear box will almost certainly incorporate reverse unless the design calls for adjustable pitch reversing propellers. The ratio of reduction is normally in the region of 2 to 1, but can vary from extremes of $1\frac{1}{2}$ to 1 up to 4 to 1. Usually a reduction reversing gear box gives a lower centreline than the engine driveshaft, although straight line reduction gears are also available, which means that the tail shaft is lower than the engine. Tail shafts may be offset if required or even raised above the engine shaft if required, by using a suitable type of gear box.

A form of coupling between engine and propeller, which enables the engine to be installed in the rear of the craft in a horizontal position if necessary, is the V drive (Fig 16). This is

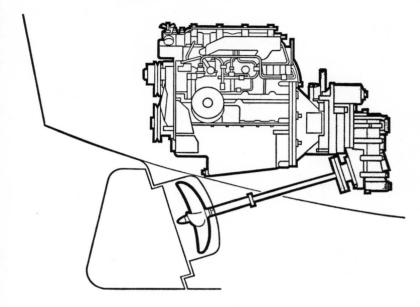

Fig 16   Nicor Vee-Drive gearbox

an angled return drive in which the engine and propeller shafts are at a shallow vee angle to each other with the latter running under or alongside the engine. Coupling of the shafts is through gears housed in an oil-tight casing and incorporating reduction and reverse gears.

Reliability, quiet running and simplicity of operation are the main requirements with any gear box. These are primarily matters for the designer, but a good deal also depends on the precision with which the gear wheels are machined. A well-designed, precision engineered gear box will do its job without an appreciable power loss penalty.

Engine manufacturers often offer a choice of gear boxes with or without reduction gears. Others supply only their own equipment. Selection is not a problem for the average boat user because the design of craft and the uses to which it is put largely determine the type of power unit, which again leads to the most suitable gear box.

In general principle marine gear boxes provide one or more of the following facilities:

(1) A direct drive from engine to propeller without reduction gear, with ahead only and with clutch to

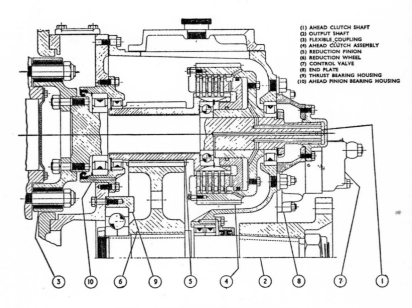

(1) AHEAD CLUTCH SHAFT
(2) OUTPUT SHAFT
(3) FLEXIBLE COUPLING
(4) AHEAD CLUTCH ASSEMBLY
(5) REDUCTION PINION
(6) REDUCTION WHEEL
(7) CONTROL VALVE
(8) END PLATE
(9) THRUST BEARING HOUSING
(10) AHEAD PINION BEARING HOUSING

Fig 17   Clutch assembly, cross section

disengage the drive. The clutch may be controlled by the operator or it may be of the centrifugal type which engages when the throttle is open and disengages when it is closed, allowing the propeller to free wheel. (A freewheeling propeller gives less drag than one which is stationary when a craft is sailing.)

164

(2) Direct drive from engine to propeller with ahead, reverse and neutral, with clutch.

(3) Reduction gear drive to propeller with ahead, reverse and neutral, with clutch (Fig 17).

There are many variations in the achievement of these basic functions and controls may be mechanically or hydraulically operated. Often engine throttle and gear—ahead, astern, neutral—is controlled by the operation of a single small hand lever situated conveniently to the helmsman's hand.

The following brief description of some of the currently available marine gear boxes will give an idea of different manufacturers' approaches to the problems of converting engine power to movement of the craft through the water under the control of the operator.

The Stuart epicyclic gear, as fitted to Stuart Turner engines up to 12hp, consists of trains of spur gears and cones. The assemblies comprise front sun wheel and forward cone, drive shaft and planet cage, clutch and control mechanism.

When forward gear is engaged the clutch body, planet cage and planet pinions lock solid and rotate at engine speed causing the drive to be transmitted per the secondary shaft to the propeller.

In neutral the propeller is free to idle.

In reverse the clutch body and planet cage lock together, the planet pinions engage with the primary sun wheel and their companion wheels drive the secondary sun wheel and the secondary shaft rotates in the opposite direction to the engine at 0·8 engine speed.

The throttle, operated by hand lever, is linked mechanically with the gear-selection mechanism so that when either forward or reverse is selected the engine operates according to the throttle setting, but in neutral engine speed is automatically reduced to idling, thus ensuring that it does not race on no load, and cannot stall when the gear is changed.

Hydraulic marine gear boxes designed to transmit full-rated torque continuously in both ahead and astern drive is the PRM,

three versions of which are marketed by Newage Engineers Ltd
of Lancashire. Optional ratios of direct drive (1 to 1, 2 to 1 and
3 to 1) are covered by models PRM100, PRM175 and PRM250.
Output rotation can be handed left or right permitting handed
propellers in twin-screw installations and rotation of the propeller
shaft while the gear box is in neutral does not have any adverse
effect due to special design features.

The casing is of heavy duty alloy cast iron, with internal
webbing for rigidity and strength, and the case hardened nickel
chrome alloy steel gears, which have shaved helical teeth for
quiet running, are housed inside the main gear box casing so
that no external reduction unit is needed. This makes for short
overall length. Only the oil pump and filter and hydraulic control
valves and lever are mounted externally. The valve block has
connections for the oil cooler which must be fitted and there is
provision for fitting an oil pressure gauge and two positions where
an impulse-type tachometer may be connected.

The multi-plate clutches are hydraulically operated and the
hydraulic circuits, as well as the lubrication, are supplied by a
gear-type pump. The hydraulic system works efficiently on any
recommended engine oil. The hydraulic control box contains
the main valve for the clutches, a relief valve and two pressure
differential valves, all easily accessible cartridge-type units. In the
event of hydraulic failure the transmission may be locked in
ahead drive as an emergency measure.

The operating lever is mounted on the control valve. It is
fully balanced and the mechanism is suitable for use with a
single-lever system such as Morse or Teleflex. The butterfly-
shaped lever allows for cable entry from either side. There is a
positive neutral position which allows for precise control of the
craft and helps in setting up the operating cables.

The input shaft is of case hardened nickel chrome alloy steel
and the output shaft of hardened and tempered nickel chrome
steel with four-hole mounting output flange. Adaptors are
supplied for fitting to flywheel housings on a large range of
engines. Each of the models may be mounted in any one of four

basic positions, that is to port with output shaft vertically below the input shaft; to starboard with the output shaft horizontal to the input shaft; to starboard with the output shaft vertically below the input shaft; and to port with the output shaft horizontal to the input shaft.

Nicor Marine Ltd of Staffordshire supply the Nicor TMP Type 12000 MK2 hydraulically operated marine gear box for direct drive as standard or with built-on reduction gear unit. The box is suitable for single-lever control systems controlling both engine speed and gear selection, and is compact and self-contained. On the direct-drive version output speed equals engine speed in ahead and 83 per cent of engine speed in astern. The built-on reduction unit with two or three pinion single helical gear trains for right- or left-handed propellers gives ratios of 2 to 1 and 3 to 1.

A built-in oil pump supplies oil under pressure for activation and forced-feed lubrication. The control valve directs high pressure oil to act on either side of an operating piston mounted on the clutch-moving element which is splined on to an annulus gear so that it can slide axially but not rotate in relation to the gear. When the clutch-moving element is engaged with the external conical surface of the output shaft all the rotating elements are locked together. This gives ahead. When the clutch-moving element is moved to the other end of its travel it engages the astern clutch lining fixed in the main casing. The annulus gear then cannot rotate and the drive is transmitted through an epicyclic gear train formed by a sun gear on the input shaft and individually rotating double planet gears mounted on pins on the output shaft, thus giving astern. For neutral the clutch-moving element does not engage being held in its central position by an automatic self-centring device acting on the operating piston. Rotation of the output shaft is then prevented by oil pressure directed behind the neutral brake.

An adjustable built-in differential relief valve keeps the operating oil at constant pressure and a full flow renewable oil filter is fitted.

The gear box is self-contained, fully automatic, needs no adjustment and minimal maintenance, gear engagement is positive with no possibility of clutch slip and allows a free propeller shaft with the engine stopped. It is designed for operation with diesel or petrol engines and adaptation parts are available for most well-known power units.

An interesting variation on the mechanical approach to the Vee drive comes from the Walter Machine Co Inc of Jersey City, USA, and whose UK agents are Golden Arrow Marine Ltd of Newhaven, Sussex.

While most conventional V drives use angle gears and housings for the V angle, the Walter V-Drives employ special coupled Cardan or Rzeppa universal joints fully encased and lubricated. A choice of V angles from 10 to 22° to suit differing requirements and a number of gear ratios are available. The gears and shafts are parallel and an idler gear allows handed rotation for twin installations.

For petrol engines the drive is through automotive Cardan-type needle bearing universal joints, while Rzeppa ball bearing constant velocity universal joints are employed for diesel power units.

Exceptional flexibility is obtained by the use of built-in double universal joints at equal angles for constant velocity. These are supported in front by a self-aligning ball bearing and spring-loaded oil seal to contain the lubricant, and a flexible joint assembly for connection to the engine. A slidable splined shaft connects these two points and eliminates strains between engine and V-Drive and provides for an ideal installation for flexibly mounted engines.

Cooling is by jacketed water covers for the smaller splash-lubricated units or by tubular oil cooler with oil-circulating pump for the larger models. In both cases there is adequate heat exchange for continuous high speed operation.

Quietness at all speeds is ensured by the use of fully hardened precision helical gears of alloy steel, the teeth being cut and shaved before and honed after heat treatment, giving accurate, smooth and quiet operation.

A conventional gear box is supplied by the Kelvin Marine Division of English Electric Diesels Ltd of Glasgow. Normally fitted to Kelvin diesel engines, it is made in two sizes known as the RG12 and the RG32, the latter having the larger power capacity.

The units operate with three shafts—the primary, the secondary and the output shaft. The first shaft is coupled direct to the engine and so rotates at the same speed and in the same direction as the engine. Identical wheels gear together the primary and secondary shafts and the latter therefore rotates at engine speed but in the opposite direction.

Mounted loosely on the primary and secondary shafts are identical toothed pinions which are in constant mesh with a gear wheel fixed on the output shaft. One, or other, of the pinions can be locked to the shaft on which it is mounted, thus transmitting torque to the output shaft in either the ahead or astern direction. Neutral is obtained with neither pinion locked as frictional drags on the opposite—rotating—parts cancel out.

Hydraulically operated, multi-disc friction clutches mounted concentrically on the shafts and housed inside the wheels, which couple the shafts together, lock the pinions on their shafts. The sizes of the pinions and output shaft-mating wheel can be varied to give different reduction ratios.

A gear-type oil pump provides oil pressure for the clutch operation and general mechanism lubrication and a manually operated control valve directs oil to one or other side of the two clutches giving ahead or astern drive as required.

The pinions and output shaft wheel are made in four sizes giving ratios of 1 to 1, 2 to 1, 2½ to 1 and 3⅛ to 1, all of which are equal ahead or astern.

Self Changing Gears Ltd of Coventry provide gear boxes for a wide range of craft and power outputs. The Type MRF700HD MkII is designed for heavy duty service in fishing boats, barges, tugs, ferries and all types of workboats, while lower capacities are catered for by the MRF250 HD MkII model. Technical, operational and constructional features are largely similar in the two units.

A sintered bronze and steel multi-plate clutch pack is used for ahead, while for astern there is a similar clutch brake arrangement and epicyclic gears. Again a multi-plate clutch-type brake is used for neutral, ensuring positive holding of the output shaft and the elimination of propeller creep.

Large diameter shafts and bearings are used to cover the 40,000hr requirements for approval by Der Norske Veritas and Lloyds.

Oil supply for clutch operation and general lubrication is provided by an internally mounted spur gear-type pump and a sump strainer and external oil filter are employed. If required a large capacity external oil cooler can be fitted.

The use of oil pressure to operate the clutches allows for remote control and single-lever operation of both engine and gear box which is available as an extra in place of the standard control.

A safety feature in the form of an emergency lock-up device, consisting of a simple-to-operate plunger unit, provides for the engagement of ahead should the hydraulic system fail.

A wide range of gears suitable for all types of pleasure craft and workboats is made by the Illinois (USA) firm Twin Disc Inc (European and Scandinavian distribution by Twin Disc Internation SA, Nivelles, Belgium). With so many units it is not possible here to give individual descriptions but each incorporates certain interesting design and practical engineering features. One of these is the unique Rubber Drive consisting of a milled lug drive spider capped with synthetic rubber blocks moulded to involute form and driven by an internal gear-driving ring bolted to the engine flywheel. To simplify installation all driving rings are made to standard SAE engine flywheel dimensions. The drive is effective in compensating for misalignment which could otherwise impose loads and stresses on gears and engine crankshaft, and quiet in operation.

Oil-cooled clutches give smooth, shockless clutch engagement with immediate response and positive neutral. Full horse power is obtained in both ahead and astern. Bearing bores and dowel holes in main housings and rear covers are machined simultaneously on production jig borers to an accuracy of 0·0002in which ensures exact centres and parallel shafting. Gears are accurately machined for quietness and efficient operation and receive a final grinding on special Maag grinders. Anti-friction ball or roller bearings are used in all units. Two opposed lip seals prevent leakage of oil to bilge, or the entry of bilge water, and seal life is prolonged by grease packed in the cavity between the two seals. Most of the larger gear units have an integral emergency feature allowing mechanical lockup of clutch giving ahead drive at half throttle should the hydraulic system fail.

The Parsons Engineering Co Ltd of Southampton provide mechanically and hydraulically operated marine reverse and reduction gears.

The mechanical Type MG4 takes the ahead drive through a multi-plate clutch actuated by a sliding cone and adjustable toggles. In ahead the whole internal mechanism revolves as a unit, leaving the bevel pinions stationary on their axes.

Astern drive is obtained through a train of bevel gears enclosed within a cage, providing opposite rotation of the propeller at the same speed as ahead. The cage is held stationary by a Ferodo lined brake band when the gear lever is pulled aft. In this position the bevel pinions rotate on their axes and reverse the action of the aft shaft.

The gear is self-locking in ahead and astern. Neutral is obtained by a spring-loaded ball and a recess in the quadrant.

Self-contained reduction gear units give ratios of 2 to 1 and 3 to 1. Three types are available for low-, medium- and high-power engines. The standard two-wheel gears reverse propeller rotation direction relative to engine crankshaft, but special three-wheel gears are available in the same ratios for handed propellers in twin-engine installations.

The reverse and reduction gears are each self-contained units and all the operating mechanisms and working parts are splash lubricated in oil-tight casings. Shaft and gear bearings are replaceable by Company-supplied spares without the need for any fitting.

The hydraulic Type HG4 MkII is fundamentally similar to the mechanically operated units, in that a multi-plate clutch provides ahead drive and a brake band and train of bevel gears the astern drive. The operating mechanism, however, consists of two servo pistons instead of the mechanical linkage and mechanism.

A Hobourn Eaton pump, located internally behind the front cover, draws oil from the gear box sump and supplies it under pressure via an oil filter to a selector valve oil chamber. The selector valve is of the piston type and is located at the rear of the top cover. Operation is by external lever, causing oil to be directed to one of two servo cylinders, one housing the piston which engages the multi-plate clutch for ahead drive, the other applying the brake for reverse drive.

The reduction gear units already described are also used with this gear.

Another well-known name in marine gear and transmission units is Borg Warner of Indiana, USA, whose products are marketed under the name of Velvet Drive. These are hydraulic transmissions in three basic configurations, In-Line, Drop-Center and V-Drive. Each incorporates the same type of ahead and astern planetary shift. The acceptable horse power input of the various models varies between 70 and 185 at 3,200rev/min for diesel engines and between 180 and 475 at 4,200rev/min for petrol engines. Various ratios and propeller rotations in relation to crankshaft are also available.

The In-Line unit has ahead and astern with or without reduction gears and, as the name implies, the output shaft is on the same centre line as the engine crankshaft. The Drop-Center has ahead and astern, a selection of reduction gears and optional propeller rotation, while the V-Drive, in the form of an integral mount with no universal joints, also gives ahead and astern and optional propeller rotation.

Common features of the transmission units are the use of planetary gears, helical gears, externally mounted oil cooler, gear-driven oil pump and positive shift. The design allows for installation at either end of the engine.

Whatever the make, today's marine transmission unit is precision built with built-in reliability taken for granted. Straightforward user maintenance is all that is needed for trouble-free operation.

CHAPTER 13

PROPELLERS

Much of the written material on propellers tends to be involved, requiring constant reference to charts, graphs and tables while one struggles through heavy narrative involving pitches, diameters and efficiencies.

While such matter is of course essential for a technical knowledge of the propeller, it is first helpful to build up a mental picture of its actual operation in the water and an understanding of the work it has to do.

At first sight it might seem that the propeller can be forgotten, it being something dealt with by the engine manufacturer and boat designer and in very many cases such an assumption is perfectly justifiable. If the craft operates at its claimed performance, if engine revs and boat speed are correct at cruising settings, fuel consumption is normal and there is no undue vibration not traceable to the engine, then all is well and the only thought the operator has about the propeller is that he shall keep it clear of ropes, anchor chains and other underwater obstructions.

But it doesn't always work out quite like that. There are a number of reasons why an owner may wish to know a little more about the propeller than that it is simply something which revolves somewhere under the boat. For example, the engine may not run at proper cruising revs, even though the boat appears to be reaching the correct cruising speed through the water. Or engine revs may be too high. Or fuel consumption may be excessive for no particularly apparent reason. Or there may be unaccountable vibration periods, and so on. It is in such circumstances that a basic knowledge of the function and operating principles of the propeller will be of value, even if it does no more than enable the owner to provide a propeller manufacturer with information essential for him to recommend a suitable replacement.

To understand how a propeller works it is first necessary to consider the movement of a boat in the medium in which it operates—water. For although water is incompressible when totally enclosed in a container, such as a sealed cylinder, it reacts to pressure by moving away from the pressure when in its natural environment. But at the same time it resists such movement and in so doing creates friction between itself and the object exerting the pressure. If an object is moved through water with violence a considerable amount of air is introduced into it which, temporarily, reduces its density and thus lessens the force of its reaction to forces acting upon it. For example, when rowing a dinghy one dips the oars and exerts a steady pull on the handles and because the resistance of the water to the blades of the oars is greater than the resistance of the water to movement of the dinghy through it, the boat moves. If, however, the dinghy is secured to some immovable object such as a mooring buoy, increased effort at the oars will soon cause such turbulence around the blades that air bubbles are introduced and as these increase the blades merely move through the water in a mass of foam with a substantial reduction in propulsive effort. When the same thing happens to a propeller it is called 'slip'.

There are several factors involved in considering the forces acting on a boat and the water in which it floats, both when it is stationary and when it is moving. But first a further clarification. There are basically two types of boats, those which displace water, ie float in it, and those which plane along the surface. (Although the hydrodynamic principles are similar, we can ignore cushion craft, hydrofoils and hydroplane-type racing craft.) In calculating propeller performance distinction must be made between displacement and planing hulls.

When a displacement hull is placed in water it sinks down

until the reaction of the water in the form of pressure equals the weight of the hull. It then floats, but the forces created by the pressure exerted, that is the weight of the hull and the resistance of the water to that weight, remain and the pressure is greatest where the water is in contact with the boat and gradually decreases as the distance from the boat increases. The pressure decreases occur roughly in layers of increasing thickness until zero. The layer in contact with the hull is at relatively high pressure. Immediately the hull moves through the water another force is introduced—friction. What happens is that the surface, or boundary layer of water (which is of course extremely thin), moves with the hull. The next layer tries to move also, but because of the effect of the next outer layer it cannot do so entirely, and so there is slip between the two, causing turbulence. This happens with decreasing effect with each succeeding layer until there is no water movement. This phenomenon creates what we know as drag. There are thus in still water two forces affecting the hull—pressure and drag. The surface area of the hull in contact with the water is known as the 'wetted area'.

The planing hull can be considered as a displacement hull when at rest or moving slowly. But when the speed has been increased sufficiently to bring it onto the plane the wetted area is substantially reduced. As the purpose of the propeller is to move the boat through water these and other factors have to be taken into consideration at the design stage in relation to the type of hull and the conditions in which it will normally be used. As the hull and propeller are operating in a liquid rather than a solid, efficiency losses are inevitable, the propeller design solution being at best a compromise. Also, because a boat's propeller operates in a liquid it is better termed propeller rather than screw, which is more easily thought of as something related to a solid. And there is an important difference in function, for the propeller is subject to slip whereas a screw in solid material is not. There are also fundamental design differences. A screw, whether square or vee shaped, merely has the thread formed in a spiral along its shank. A propeller, on the other hand, is designed as an aerofoil with blades having a proper aerofoil section so that they give lift as well as thrust and a calculable drag component.

In theory pitch is the distance the propeller will advance in one revolution. That is, a propeller of 12in pitch will in one complete revolution move forward 1ft. In practice this is seldom if ever achieved, and if it is it will be in certain water and boat speed conditions which in no way increase propeller efficiency. Such conditions can be ignored in considering propeller operation in small craft.

Comparison between the screw in a solid and a propeller in water will help to make the pitch function clear. A wood screw, for example, when turned one complete revolution twists itself into the wood a distance equal to the pitch of its thread. It can do this because the wood is an unyielding material which does not move in relation to the screw. Water is a different proposition altogether. It offers only limited resistance to movement of a solid object through it.

The nearest one could get to the actual as opposed to the theoretical pitch of a propeller would be to have it turning at its correct speed (rev/min) in still water and unattached to a boat or any other object. Then as the blades 'bite' into the water and the forces of lift, thrust and drag come into operation, the propeller moves ahead. But because of the pressure exerted on the water some of it moves rearward and this reduces the effective pitch, creating the phenomenon known as propeller 'slip'. In this, purely theoretical, example the slip will be relatively small, depending on the design of the blades, water density (whether it is fresh or sea water and the depth at which the propeller is operating), water temperature, the drag factor of the blade aerofoil section, the effect of water flow over the propeller hub, and so on.

When the propeller is attached to a boat and turned by an engine over which, in relation to the operation of the propeller at theoretical optimum efficiency, one has only limited control, a number of other unwanted happenings take place which adversely affect the propeller, lowering its efficiency and reducing its actual pitch. But before looking at these let us examine what it is we are trying to achieve. We will assume still water conditions and a displacement hull with an engine designed to run at 1,800rev/min normal operation (it can of course be throttle up or down to give full power or low speed when required, but it is not necessary to calculate for these conditions), and at this speed gives X shaft horse power (shp) which as the twisting force exerted on the engine drive shaft is expressed as torque, or twisting force, in foot pounds (ft lbf). Let us also say that if this power can be effectively harnessed into propulsive effort it will push our hull through the water at Y knots.

We now have to choose, or design, a propeller which will meet these requirements, pushing the boat through the water at Y knots while allowing the engine to run at 1,800rev/min and so absorbing and using the power output without causing vibration, power loss or engine speed variations.

Propeller design is of course a highly technical matter and quite outside the scope of this book. Also it would most likely be that, for the conditions of our example, a propeller manufacturer would be able to supply a propeller of pitch and diameter near enough correct for the job, from stock. In fact there are standard reference tables available from which the near enough correct propeller may be chosen to suit different combinations of engine power output and operating rev/min and hull speed. If, for example, our theoretical boat was a 40ft cruiser of 10ft beam and 3ft 8in draught and the engine gave 36hp, a three-bladed, 22in diameter propeller of 14in pitch turning at 1,000rev/min would give us a (theoretical) hull speed of 8¼ knots. Using available tables in this way is to take advantage of a mass of data accumulated by design and practical considerations and can give quite usable and even accurate results. In all probability this method will be the designer's first approach to the problem and it is almost certainly the method a propeller manufacturer would use when supplying, or suggesting, a propeller to meet specific conditions. But what happens if when the propeller is fitted to our example boat we get 9¼ knots and the engine runs at 1,650rev/min? To understand how this could occur we have to look at some of the problems facing the propeller designer.

If hull were of absolutely clean design and the propeller turned only in undisturbed water and if operation were always at engine cruising rev/min and hull speed, the designer's task would be relatively simple. Unfortunately things are not so easy. Other factors exert an influence and affect propeller performance. For example:

> The hull may be clean enough in design and in actual operation, moving through the water with very little upset, but the deadwood immediately in front of the propeller may disturb the water flowing over it.
>
> *or*
>
> The hull may cause some turbulence aft.
>
> *or*
>
> The propeller itself may be at fault, the blade pitch angle may be wrong, or the area of the blades too large, or the blades set up interference with each other, or the blades may be bad in section, resulting in high drag, or the diameter may be too large or too small.
>
> *or*
>
> Perhaps the hull may carry an amount of water along with it at cruising or higher speeds, thus giving the propeller an effective pitch different from the designer's.

Then there are problems for the designer and he has to compromise in finding a solution. For instance a propeller design which gave near perfect performance in getting a boat moving initially (in which conditions affecting propeller operation change continuously from zero speed to cruising speed) would be quite unsuitable for continuous economic cruising at correct hull speed and engine revs. Propeller performance is also adversely affected by the behaviour of the boat in a seaway, when pitching and rolling and plunging headlong into a sea impose forces on the hull which try to change its speed and direction through the water and in which the propeller is continually operating in different water depths.

These outline considerations give some idea of the difficulties facing the designer in attempting to create the right propeller for any given boat. In our example where the hull speed is 9¼ knots and engine rev/min 1,650 instead of 8¼ knots at 1,800 rev/min, the most likely cause would be a propeller o ítoo large diameter, causing it to turn too slowly. Instead of 1,000rev/min it is, say, only doing 900rev/min and holding the engine speed down to 1,650. On the other hand there would seem to be a plus in that we are getting an extra knot in hull speed, so why not leave things as they are? There are several reasons. If the hull speed is 8¼ knots a disproportionately greater amount of power will be needed to push it along at 9¼ knots. The reason for this is that every boat has a natural water speed closely related to the waterline length and other factors such as shape, wetted area, weight and so on. Any attempt to obtain a higher speed calls for an excessive increase in power and however much more push is given the hull will not reach more than a knot or so above its natural speed. If, when this is achieved, still more power is used, propeller slip becomes excessive and although there may appear an impressive upheaval and disturbance in the water, fuel and mechanical effort is merely being wasted.

It is desirable to run the engine at the engine manufacturer's recommended speeds because he and the boat designer have got together and worked out hull speed and the power needed to obtain it. Then calculations are made to provide a propeller to bring these two factors together. If all the factors are right the designed boat performance will occur at economical engine rev/min and power output, fuel consumption will be moderate and general operation free from tiresome vibrations, excessive engine noise and possible overheating. And operation at different engine speeds, ie manoeuvring at low speed, or at full power if necessary, will be as efficient as can be.

Apart from the involved intricacies of propeller design, there are certain basic elements the boat owner can assimilate without too much technical involvement. Slip is expressed as a percentage of efficiency. No propeller is 100 per cent efficient, as will be appreciated from the factors affecting its operation already described. Slip is normally in the region of 10–30 per cent depending on the type of boat and its speed and the speed of the propeller. A reasonable slip figure for a full bodied displacement hull with the propeller running at up to about 1,000rev/min would be around 12–15 per cent or 16 per cent. Faster-running propellers and finer-lined craft will have a slip figure in the region of 20–30 per cent, while high-speed craft will again show a reduction of propeller slip of around 10–12 per cent.

It is, of course, a matter of providing the right type of propeller for the particular craft. Slow vessels use a slow-running propeller of relatively coarse pitch, whereas fine pitch is needed for high-speed craft with fast-running propellers.

Pitch angle is the angle the blades are set at in relation to the centre line of the propeller hub. Because the blades are twisted to obtain constant pitch throughout their length, the pitch angle varies along the blade length and it is measured at a point two-thirds of propeller diameter. It is at this part of the blade that the maximum amount of work is done. Further towards the tip and again inwards towards the hub efficiency decreases, particularly in way of the hub which tends to set up its own turbulence. Broadly speaking the faster a propeller runs the finer will be its pitch angle.

There are other factors of propeller design—blade area, shape and thickness. Each can adversely affect performance. If the blades are too wide they may cause interference between them, upsetting the water flow round them and producing turbulence. If in section they are too thick they will be harder for the engine to push through the water and it therefore may run slower than its rated speed. Blade thickness is more critical in high-revving propellers. In slow-turning propellers, such as will be found on the beamy fishing vessel, running at around 800rev/min, quite a wide tolerance of blade thickness can be accommodated before performance suffers.

Propellers

The reaction to a turning propeller, known as propeller torque, can have a marked effect, causing the hull to move in a circle unless corrected with the rudder. Torque is most noticeable with large-diameter propellers and if it is excessive, necessitating large rudder offset, the extra drag will reduce the speed of the boat. Drag is also set up by the propeller and its shaft and bracket.

Propeller design and construction can hardly be called an exact science and the device is not necessarily the best or most efficient means of converting engine power to movement of a boat in water. There are of course other propulsion systems as outlined in Chapter 12. But the propeller has been dealt with in some detail because it is still the most universally used system and, relatively, the cheapest. It also has that advantage of being easy to alter if the hull or engine performance is not what it should be. In general practice it is unlikely that the average boat owner will wish, or need, to change or experiment with his propeller, but should things not seem right he will have enough basic information in this chapter to discuss possibilities with engine manufacturer, designer or propeller maker. The sort of information required by a propeller manufacturer to enable him to supply a propeller which will have a good chance of giving satisfactory performance provides a neat summary of the various factors involved. These include:

Description of the boat, ie displacement type or V hull, high-speed cruiser, racing craft, motor sailer, yacht, etc.

Dimensions—length overall, length water line, beam, draught.

Displacement.

Shape of the stern, ie transom, canoe, etc.

Position of propeller, type of bracket and arrangement of shafting.

Full details of any deadwood ahead of the propeller.

The desired hull speed with details if with an existing propeller this is not being reached, or is being exceeded.

Engine horse power and maker's specified rev/min at this output.

Details of bore, stroke, number of cylinders and whether petrol or diesel, two stroke or four stroke.

Director of rotation of propeller viewed from aft, bearing in mind that if a reduction gear is used this will usually turn the propeller in the opposite direction to that obtained with direct drive. A guide on possible diameter will also be required. It must be stated what maximum diameter would be to allow not less than one inch clearance from the nearest part of the hull.

If the propeller is required to replace an existing one the number of blades should be stated. Most cruising craft, displacement or high speed V type will use three-bladed propellers.

Such are the basic factors required by a propeller supplier who will normally provide a form for the enquirer to complete.

So far we have dealt with the fixed pitch-type of propeller. Adjustable, variable and reversing pitch propellers are also produced as a means of obtaining optimum performance at varying shaft horse powers and hull speeds, such as occur when operating slowly for fishing, or berthing, accelerating or using power to punch a foul tide. Sometimes, too, the reversing pitch propeller is used instead of a reversing gear box. Yet again, folding propellers are available for yachts to minimise drag when sailing.

However, such units require special and relatively complicated control mechanisms and so the cost of the equipment and the work involved in installation makes them somewhat expensive. One company, Hamble Foundry Ltd, produces an entirely automatic variable pitch propeller for yachts which is activated by centrifugal forces and the water flow and so requires no mechanical linkage for operation.

The unit is known as the Hamblematic folding propeller and its op ration is very simple. When the engine controls are placed in the 'ahead' position and the throttle opened, centrifugal forces acting on the turning propeller hold the blades open and drive is obtained. If the engine is shut off the water flow past the propeller resulting from the forward motion of the boat causes the blades to fold together in a streamlined shape trailing at the end of the propeller shaft, and in this position drag is minimal. This would be the position of the propeller if the craft was under sail, engine off. Selecting reverse and applying engine power again brings in centrifugal forces to open the blades.

The Hamblematic propeller offers several advantages for both cruising and racing craft. It produces only low drag when sailing. Its operation is instant and automatic immediately engine power is applied in either 'ahead' or 'astern', it has no manual control and costly mechanical linkage and, as the hub is bored to fit standard propeller shaft tapers and threads, no special skill or equipment is required for fitting.

A variable pitch and reversing propeller which will transmit and absorb $\frac{3}{4}$hp per 100rev/min giving, for example, $7\frac{1}{2}$hp at 1,000rev/min, 15hp at 2,000rev/min, is made by Watermota Ltd. The mechanical arrangement of this unit consists of a $\frac{3}{4}$in diameter inner shaft which transmits the torque, and a 1in diameter outer operating tube. The propeller is available in the standard diameters, 10in, 11in, and 12in, and may be either left or right handed. The equipment is supplied as a standard set and includes 5ft propeller shaft, thrust block and control mechanism. Increased torque up to $1\frac{1}{4}$hp at 100rev/min can be transmitted if a stainless steel shaft and operating head are used. The propellers are designed to operate most efficiently at speeds between 1,200 and

1,500rev/min and when the motive power is a high-speed engine a reduction gear should be used. The pitch control has a locking device incorporated by which the propeller may be locked at the most suitable pitch. Also available is a 'sailing' version of the propeller which has a rack and pinion blade-twisting mechanism by which the blades can be fully feathered to reduce drag to a minimum when the craft is under sail.

SPM variable pitch and reversing propellers up to 8ft diameter are made by Slack & Parr (Marine) Ltd. With a capacity up to 800bhp, they are designed particularly to meet the exacting conditions and widely varying loads encountered by working craft such as fishing boats and tugs. The operating mechanism consists of a sliding control rod within the propeller shaft. Axial movement of the rod and propeller crosshead is converted into rotary movement of the blades through blocks located on crank pins sliding in transverse slots machined in the crosshead. Because working craft often operate in waters containing suspended sand and gritty particles the SPM propellers are specially sealed against the entry of such abrasive matter. While small units are mechanically activated, hydraulic operation is employed for the larger propellers and when necessary reduction gears are employed between engine and propeller shaft.

The title of 'Coaster Units' is given to a range of variable pitch, reversing and feathering propellers made by P.N.P. Duerr Ltd. Available with either direct drive or 2:1 reduction, with or without clutch, they are suitable for engines up to 100bhp at 2,000 shaft rev/min. Controls may be hydraulic, or hand- or servo-assisted teleflex for remote control from the steering position, or, direct hand control.

Extensive research is now programmed at Newcastle-on-Tyne University into the operation of ducted propellers, which is a system used since the 1930s for ship propulsion. Propeller efficiency may be increased if more water can be made to pass between the blades. Surrounding a propeller with a hollow duct ring causes an increase in water flow and thrust is also obtained from the duct.

Propellers

The prime reason for the current research is the increasing size of tankers which require larger and larger propellers. There is, however, a limit to propeller size for technical reasons and the answer so far has been to fit two smaller propellers. It is hoped that research will show how a single-ducted propeller may produce adequate thrust.

Although this is a development applicable to commercial shipping it is not unlikely that a successful outcome to the investigations would result in units being produced for smaller craft.

CHAPTER 14

ENGINE INSTALLATION

There are certain fundamental requirements involved in marine-engine installation which will ensure a successful job and trouble-free operation. As will be seen there is a good deal more to it than simply putting the engine in the boat and connecting the drive shaft to the propeller: The principles apply whether the engine is a manufactured marine power unit, a professional marination or a conversion of an automobile engine. The main factors are: alignment with shafting, protection of the engine and ancillary equipment and fittings, insulation of the engine compartment against noise and smells, correct installation of fuel tanks and pipe lines, ignition assemblies and wiring, cooling, exhaust systems, location of ancillary equipment and controls, and fire protection.

These factors can be analysed under a number of broad headings, the first of which covers engine mounting which is closely allied to shafting and alignment.

MOUNTING

Alignment of the engine with the propeller shaft, the first basic requirement, is linked to the way the engine is to be secured in the boat, which leads at once to consideration of engine bearers.

Normally of timber—oak, pitch or oregon pine, or other woods of similar characteristics—they must be of adequate section and length to bear the weight of the engine, absorb vibration and distribute the loads evenly throughout the hull. Cross bracing or knees and flooring may be required to absorb side forces caused by engine torque, particularly in the case of single- and twin-cylinder power units. It is essential that the bearers cannot 'spread' sideways.

The overall length, section and height of the bearers is governed by factors such as the size of the hull, the amount of room fore and aft of the engine when in position, the size of the flywheel, depth of the sump and the maximum permitted angle of the engine relative to the horizontal.

This latter point will be specified by the engine manufacturer and must not be exceeded. Nor should an engine be installed 'nose down' as this can cause cooling troubles due to air locks in water jackets at the aft end of the cylinder head.

In glass fibre and steel boats engine bearers are usually built in when the hull is made and essentially the work is done to full professional boat building standards. The importance of adequate engine bearers properly located, secured and braced cannot be over stressed, for they are the link between the power unit and hull and on them largely depends the smooth, trouble-free engine operation always expected, but sometimes never achieved.

With wooden bearers metal pressure plates are necessary to prevent the engine-mounting feet (normally plain metal brackets bolted to the sides of the engine) digging into the timber when pulling down on the mounting bolts or by vibration under running conditions. The plates should be rectangular or strip steel or angle iron running the whole length of each bearer, to which they are secured with coach screws driven into the timber. To take the engine mounting bolts, 'clearance fit' holes are drilled in the plates in line with those in the engine's mounting brackets.

The engine is then positioned with the mounting feet positioned on the pads and secured to the bearers with bolts. With the possible exception in the case of very low-powered units used principally as auxiliaries in sailing yachts, coach screws should not be used for engine holding down as they tend to work loose under the effects of engine torque and vibration.

The bolts should be as long as can be accommodated by the depth of the bearers and protrude through to morticed holes cut to accommodate the nuts. Again metal pressure pads must be used above the nuts to stop them biting into the timber when tightened. The degree of tightness depends to some extent on the density of the timber, but must always be sufficient to securely hold the engine at all engine speeds and under whatever may be the forces acting on the hull, but not so tight that the timber is crushed.

Flexible mountings are often used to insulate engine vibration from the hull as far as possible, particularly in craft of the lighter type of construction. Flexible couplings must also then be used in the tailshaft to accommodate engine movement. A flexible mounted engine installation is not as straightforward as it may seem at first sight. Engine manufacturers offering flexible mountings have usually only arrived at satisfactory schemes for their power units after considerable research and experiment. The engine maker or qualified marine engine supplier or installer should always be consulted when flexible mounting is planned or if trouble arises with existing installations. Badly designed or improperly carried out, the flexible installation can cause more rather than less vibration and put unnecessary strains on the tail shaft and bearings. Nor can liberties be taken with the tailshaft alignment which must be just as accurately carried out as for fixed-type mounting. Flexible couplings are usually advisable with the V drive system of propulsion with flexible couplings or universal joints between engine output shaft and V drive unit.

PROPELLER SHAFT ALIGNMENT

Whatever method of engine mounting is used, solid or flexible, true alignment of the propeller shaft with the engine or gearbox output shaft has to be achieved. Incorrect alignment will cause overheating and wear in bearings and vibration and unnecessary loadings on components in the assembly.

A problem in obtaining accurate alignment arises because a

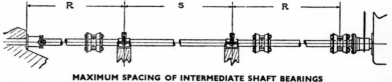

MAXIMUM SPACING OF INTERMEDIATE SHAFT BEARINGS

SHAFT	1″	1¼″	1½″	1¾″	1⅞″	2″	2¼″	2½″	3″	3½″	4″
R	4′ 6″	5′ 0″	5′ 3″	5′ 6″	6′ 3″	7′ 3″	8′ 3″	8′ 6″	5′ 0″	5′ 6″	6′ 0″
S	5′ 0″	5′ 6″	6′ 0″	6′ 3″	7′ 0″	8′ 0″	9′ 0′	9′ 6″	10′ 6″	12′ 0″	15′ 0″

Fig 18   Typical shafting installation showing spacing of intermediate shaft bearings

boat is not a positively rigid structure. Dependent on the type of construction the lines of the hull may be quite considerably different when the craft is in the water normally loaded, to when it is hauled up ashore. Therefore when an engine installation is done in a boatyard, as it often is, an alignment check must be made a few days after launching. It is quite unsound to assume that all will be as it was on dry land.

The position of the engine on the bearers, its angle fore and aft and degree of tilt athwartships is normally adjusted by placing metal shims under the mounting feet and so raising them on the bearers. By adding or removing shims the position of the engine relative to the propeller shaft can be corrected until all is true and in line. In larger installations metal wedges may be used instead of shims.

Final coupling with the stern gear is best carried out after the boat, whatever may be the materials of its construction, has been afloat for some days. With the coupling bolts removed the propeller shaft is turned and checked for true movement axially with no displacement from centre of the half coupling. The usual method is to use a straight edge and check vertical and lateral alignment at four 90° positions. Then, with a feeler gauge between the two half couplings, angular alignment is tested again in four positions 90° apart. If the propeller shaft is rotating truly any out of alignment at the two half couplings must be corrected

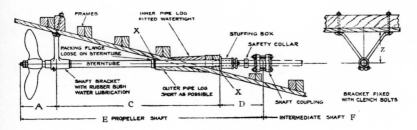

TABLE OF DIMENSIONS

Shaft	Stern Tube	Hole	Packing Flange	Stuffing Box Flange	A	D	Z
1″	1 5/16″	1 7/16″	2 1/8″ Sq.	3″×2 1/2″	6 1/4″	8″	6 1/4″
1 1/8″	1 1/2″	1 5/8″	2 1/2″ ,,	3 1/4″×2 1/2″	7 1/4″	9″	7 1/4″
1 1/4″	1 5/8″	1 3/4″	2 5/8″ ,,	3 1/2″×2 1/2″	8″	10″	8 1/4″
1 3/8″	1 3/4″	1 7/8″	2 5/8″ ,,	3 1/2″×2 1/2″	8 1/2″	11″	9″
1 1/2″	1 7/8″	2″	3″ ,,	3 3/4″×2 3/4″	9 1/4″	12″	10″
1 5/8″	2″	2 1/4″	3″ ,,	4″×3 1/4″	10 1/4″	13″	10″
2″	2 1/4″	2 1/2″	3 1/2″ ,,	5″×3 1/2″	12 1/4″	16″	11″
2 1/4″	2 5/16″	2 3/4″	3 1/2″ ,,	5 1/2″×4 1/4″	14 1/4″	18″	14 1/2″
2 1/2″	2 13/16″	3 1/4″	4 1/4″ ,,	5 1/2″×4 1/2″	15 3/4″	20″	15″
3″	3 1/2″	4″	5 1/4″ ,,	5 1/2″ Sq.	18 1/4″	20″	16 1/4″
3 1/2″	4 1/4″	4 1/2″	5 1/2″ ,,	6 1/4″ ,,	21 1/4″	20″	20″
4″	5″	5 1/2″	6 1/4″ ,,	9″ dia.	23 3/4″	28″	23″
4 1/2″	5 1/2″	5 3/4″	7″ ,,	10″ dia.	26 1/2″	30″	—

The propeller clearance should be equal at least to the diameter of the shaft. Both the stuffing box and the packing flange should be close to the planking as shown at "X". The outer pipe log should be trimmed down to the size of the packing flange. The dimension "D", as given on the table, is the minimum and it is advisable to allow more where possible.

Fig 19 Typical twin screw or side shafting installation with table of dimensions

by adjusting the position of the engine by means of the shims or wedges.

STERNGEAR

The sterngear installation includes all the components immediately aft of the engine drive shaft, including the propeller.

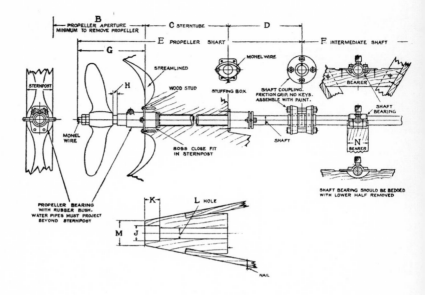

TABLE OF DIMENSIONS

Propeller Shaft	B	D	Clutch Neutral		J	K	L	M	N	Propeller Bearing Flange	Stuffing Box Flange	Shaft Coupling dia. & length
			G	H								
1"	10"	8"	7¼"	⅝"	2"	1¹³⁄₁₆"	1⁷⁄₁₆"	3½"	2"	4⁵⁄₁₆"×2¼"	3"×2¼"	3½"×3½"
1¼"	11¼"	9"	8¼"	⁷⁄₁₆"	2¹⁄₁₆"	2⁷⁄₁₆"	1½"	3½"	2¼"	4¾"×2¼"	3½"×2¼"	3½"×3½"
1½"	13"	10"	9¼"	⅝"	2½"	2¼"	1½"	4"	2¼"	4¾"×2¼"	3½"×2¼"	4¼"×4¼"
1⅝"	13½"	11"	9¹¹⁄₁₆"	¹¹⁄₁₆"	2½"	2½"	1½"	4¼"	2½"	4¾"× 3"	3½"×2⅝"	4¼"×4¼"
1¾"	15"	12"	11"	¾"	2⅝"	2½"	2"	4½"	3"	5"×3¼"	3½"×2¾"	4¼"×4¼"
1⅞"	16"	13"	11½"	¹³⁄₁₆"	2¾"	2¹¹⁄₁₆"	2¼"	4½"	3¼"	5¼"×3½"	4"×3¼"	5¼"×5¼"
2"	19½"	16"	14½"	1"	3¼"	3⁵⁄₁₆"	2¼"	5¼"	4"	5¼"×4¼"	5"×3½"	6¼"×6¼"
2¼"	22½"	18"	16½"	1¼"	2¹³⁄₁₆"	3¼"	2⅝"	6¼"	4½"	6¼"×4¼"	5½"×4¼"	7¼"×7¼"
2½"	24½"	20"	18"	1½"	4⁵⁄₁₆"	4"	3¹³⁄₁₆"	7¼"	4"	7¼"×5¼"	5½"×4½"	7½"×7½"

Fig 20   Single-screw shafting installation, plain shaft, friction-grip coupling, with dimension table

While there are many variations possible in the assembly and layout of a sterngear, the main components are relatively standardised. These are the propeller and the propeller shaft,

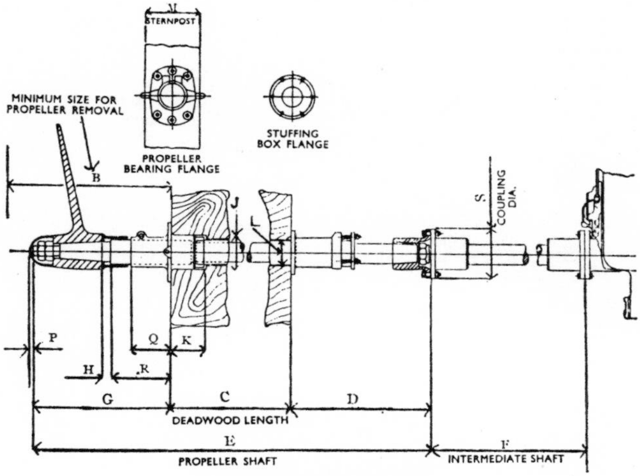

TABLE OF DIMENSIONS

Propeller Shaft Dia.	B	D	G	H	J	K	L	M	N See Sheet 13	P	Q	R	Propeller Bearing Flange	Stuffing Box Flange	S Shaft Coupling Dia.	
2″	19½″	17″	14¼″	1″	3½″	3 3/16″	2½″	6⅝″	4″	—	4″	5¾″	5⅞″×4⅛″	5″×3¾″	8¼″	—
2¼″	22½″	18″	16½″	1⅛″	3 13/16″	3½″	2¾″	6¾″	4″	—	4½″	6¾″	6⅜″×4½″	5⅜″×4¼″	8¼″	—
2½″	24½″	20″	18″	1¼″	4 5/16″	4″	3 15/16″	7½″	4″	—	5″	7½″	7¼″×5⅛″	5⅞″×4⅝″	8¼″	10″
3″	29″	20″	21⅛″	1⅜″	4¾″	5″	4″	9″	4″	⅝″	6″	9″	8½″×5¾″	5¾″ sq.	8¼″	10″
3½″	34″	20″	24½″	1⅝″	5⅝″	5½″	4½″	10″	4″	¾″	7″	10½″	9¾″×6¾″	6½″ sq.	8¼″	10″
4″	38″	28″	27¾″	1¾″	7″	6½″	5¼″	12″	—	¾″	8″	12″	12″×9″	9″ dia.	—	10″
4½″	42½″	30″	31″	1⅞″	7½″	7″	5¾″	13″	—	1″	9″	13½″	13″×10″	10″ dia.	—	10″

Fig 21 Single-screw shafting installation, taper shaft, bolted coupling, with dimension table

the stern tube, intermediate shafts, bearings, thrust blocks and shaft logs (Figs 18–22).

Mention has already been made of the necessity to properly align the propeller shaft with the engine. The purpose of the sterngear is to maintain this alignment, absorb propeller thrust, provide a means of bearing lubrication and convert the power of the engine into movement of the boat through the water.

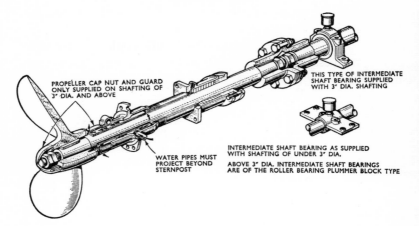

Fig 22   Typical stern-gear arrangement

The propeller bearing is lubricated by sea water and it should require no attention after installation. The cutless bush (a brass shell with a fluted rubber lining) is held in the bearing by a clamp bolt. Water for circulation through the bush enters the bearing through two small pipes fixed into the bearing and angled to suit the water stream when the boat moves forward.

Sternposts should be of recommended widths and faired away above and below the propeller bearing to streamline the flow of water to the propeller and so improve efficiency. Even better streamlining can be obtained by fixing extensions to the sternpost and then fairing them away to encourage the flow of water near the propeller.

In Chapter 6 corrosion by electrolytic action is dealt with in detail. It is important that the metals used in the sterngear are compatible with each other and with the hull or, if this is not always possible, that sacrificial plates are used. Consideration of electrolytic action determines the type of materials for sterngear components according to the material of which the hull is constructed. Typical examples are as follows:

Wood hulls

Propeller shaft and propeller, manganese bronze; stern tube, manganese bronze or brass; bearings, white metal or water-lubricated rubber, resin-bonded fabric, nylon or bronze; bearing housings, manganese bronze or gun metal; fastenings, manganese bronze, monel metal, aluminium or bronze; under water and skin fittings, manganese bronze or gun metal.

Alternative specifications for wood hulls could be: propeller shaft, stainless steel or monel metal; propeller, manganese bronze or gun metal; stern tube, manganese bronze, gun metal or brass; bearings, white metal, water-lubricated rubber, resin-bonded fabric, nylon or bronze; bearing housings, manganese bronze or gun metal; fastenings, manganese bronze or stainless steel with gun metal; under water and skin fittings, manganese bronze or gun metal.

Steel hulls

Propeller shafts must be zinc-sprayed manganese bronze, cadmium or zinc-sprayed mild steel, stainless steel or monel metal; propeller, zinc-sprayed cast iron, manganese bronze, zinc or gun metal; stern tubes, steel or zinc-sprayed cast iron; bearings white metal, water-lubricated rubber, resin-bonded fabric, nylon or bronze; bearing housings, zinc-sprayed cast iron; fastenings, stainless or galvanised steel; under water skin fittings; zinc-sprayed cast iron or steel.

Aluminium alloy hulls

Propeller shafts, stainless steel, monel metal, cadmium-plated or zinc-sprayed mild steel or heavy zinc-sprayed manganese bronze; propeller, aluminium alloy, a suitable specification being BS 1490-LM6, or manganese bronze provided zinc sacrificial rings or plates are attached to the bearing housing and hull in the vicinity of the propeller; stern tubes, aluminium alloy, a suitable specification being BS 1471-NT6; bearings, white metal with stainless steel retaining screws, rubber moulded or pressed in aluminium alloy housing, resin-bonded fabric or nylon; bearing housings, aluminium alloy, a suitable specification being BS 1490-LM6; fastenings, stainless steel; under water and skin fittings, aluminium alloy, again a suitable specification being BS 1490-LM6.

Aluminium alloy hulls should have similar material hull

fittings, but if these have to be gun metal or manganese bronze these fittings must be heavy zinc sprayed and insulating washers of a material such as resin-bonded fabric coated with barium chromate compound to specification DTD 369 must be used between the fittings and the hull. Fastenings for these fittings should be steel, stainless or galvanised.

Glass fibre hulls

The specification throughout may be the same as for wood or aluminium alloy hulls.

Having dealt so far with the requirements for getting the engine into the hull, properly secured and correctly lined up with the propeller shaft, and covered in some detail the vital matters of sterngear and hull fittings and materials compatible with different hull materials, we can consider the services needed for the engine to operate efficiently and in safety. These details cover items such as fuel supply, exhaust and cooling systems, steering and controls, proper ventilation, silencing and fire prevention. An internal combustion engine requires a constant supply of more or less volatile high to medium fire risk, odorous fuel and because it is converting such fuel into power, the noise, vibration and smell potentials are high. To prevent these evils two things are needed: correct installation and regular maintenance.

FUEL SUPPLY

The fuel system begins with the tank which should be constructed from the right type of material for the fuel to be used and be placed as low in the boat and as far away from the engine as possible. If the fuel is diesel oil the tank should be made of terne plate, lead coated or plain steel, black iron or glass reinforced self-quenching resin to BS 476. Galvanised iron and copper must not be used for diesel fuel tanks.

Petrol tanks may be terne plate, lead-coated steel, galvanised mild steel or monel metal, or brass or copper. In all metal tanks joints and seams must be brazed or welded, rolled and soldered, or riveted and soldered.

To prevent excessive fuel surge tanks holding more than 20gal require internal baffles arranged so that areas between them are not greater capacity than 3ft³.

Tanks must rest on adequate bearers to which they should be rigidly fixed so that no movement is possible whatever the motion of the boat and the installation should allow enough room for inspection and removal if necessary. In a small boat it is seldom possible to provide easy access all round a tank, but its complete removal should be possible. It is not sound policy to build the boat round the tank.

The fuel tank fittings—taps, filters, fuel cocks—must be leak proof and positive in action, particularly in the 'off' position. They also have to be accessible so that filters and sediment cups can be regularly cleaned.

In small boats and racing-type yachts in which engines of low horsepower are used, the fuel feed is often by gravity. This is not really ideal because the fuel has then to flow from the bottom of the tank, and it is there that a tap must be placed. If a tap, or the tap fitting, develops a leak, gravity ensures that fuel will drip out into the boat. Often such a fuel escape goes unnoticed for quite a time because the defective component 'weeps' rather than drips steadily. Regular inspection is the answer and a nose sensitive to any stronger-than-normal fuel smells. Most engines are odorous to some degree but with attention and regular cleaning smells can be kept within tolerable limits. Usually the filter is the glass-bowl-type and regular cleaning-out is necessary. If the tank position is such that this tap cannot be easily reached, a second tap is needed, fitted as near the tank as possible. The purpose of locating a tap, or taps, immediately under or in the bottom of the tank is to completely isolate the fuel supply from the engine and supply line so that when it is not wanted it remains only in the tank. To this end a recommended way of stopping a gravity-fed engine, except on a temporary basis, is to turn off the fuel at the tank and let the engine run the fuel line system dry.

But in some systems this can lead to air locks which cause difficulties in re-starting engines which do not have a fuel pump.

The most satisfactory and potentially safest method is to pump fuel from tank to engine. Then the fuel is drawn from the top of the tank leaving the bottom free of leak-potential holes and taps. A recommended arrangement is to locate the feed pipe in the centre of the tank and link it direct to an engine-driven fuel lift pump through one or more filters, the one nearest the tank being of the glass bowl or dished sludge trap type. Engine manufacturers and marinisers usually provide information on fuel line and filter arrangements and their recommendations should be followed. Whatever system is used the points to guard against are leaks, dirt in the fuel and the possibility of air locks, any of which will cause uneven running, loss of power and difficulty or failure in starting.

Regular inspection of all fuel lines is essential for safety and comfort aboard. Nothing is more unpleasant than a permanent smell of engine fuel and even slight 'sweating' of a fuel tap or joint can cause this. Every precaution should be taken to prevent fuel getting into the bilges and dropping onto the engine tray. When seepage occurs from a carburettor or in diesel engines in which excess fuel exudes from the atomisers some system of collecting the drippings may be fitted. Often this is simply a suitable container, glass or metal, preferably with a screw lid, or even an open top, placed under the excess fuel flow so that this either drops direct into the container or is fed in by a piece of suitable piping. Then the container can be removed periodically and the excess fuel, if clean, poured back into the fuel tank. Whatever way it is done some method should be used to stop fuel getting from the engine into the bilges. Alternatively, if piping is used to return fuel leaking off from diesel fuel injectors to the tank, or if such leakage is led direct to the fuel pump return pipe, the flow must be so arranged that such fuel always re-enters at the top of the tank.

Other considerations in the fuel supply cover its introduction into the tank which should be via an oil-resisting hose with permanent deck fitting, led, if the fuel capacity is large, to the bottom of the fuel tank, and fixed with suitable quality clips. The deck fitting must have a watertight cap clearly marked with the type of fuel used and a wire gauze strainer in the pipe.

A vent to outside atmosphere is necessary. In small tanks the hole in the tank filler cap will be adequate but on large tanks a vent pipe is required, positioned so that sea or rain water cannot get into it.

If a contents gauge of the visual type is used, rather than one of electronic operation, it must not be glass due to the breakage risk. In simple installations a dipstick may be used.

All fuel piping should be of annealed copper tube, except where flexible pipe is used or inserted in the line to prevent damage through vibration, in which case such piping must be a type approved for use as fuel line and the fuel tank electrically bonded to the engine. The size of piping is important. It must be correct for the engine and installation layout and here it may be wise to check with the manufacturer. If flexible piping is not used the copper pipe is coiled where it connects to the engine.

There are two main risks to fuel lines, chafing and actual physical damage. Securing all pipe runs at frequent intervals to prevent any movement and keeping radii at bends correct for the diameter of piping is essential. No fuel pipe should ever be under external pressure or tension.

Fuel-pipe joints are very important. The golden principle is to have as few as possible. The necessary ones must be easily accessible and supported by fixing clips placed at not more than 6in on each side. Joints must never be made with soft solder which is liable to fracture and lead to leakage, or 'weeping'. Brazing is the only safe method of attaching unions and fittings to the copper pipes. Or the metal-to-metal type are safe if properly secured. Pipe connections should never be used where pipe bends are a possible alternative.

All engines except the crankcase compression type (two stroke) should be fitted with flame traps and screened drip trays are required under all carburettors other than the down-draught type.

Finally, underneath the power unit there must be an oil-tight drip tray of sufficient size to cover the total under area of the engine and gear box, located in such a way that it can be got at for cleaning. The tray should be as deep as can be accommodated under the propeller shaft. Suitable materials are metal or reinforced plastics, but never copper because of electrolysis risk. Metal or glass reinforced plastic hulls provide the exception to the need for a drip tray if oil-tight bulkheads are installed fore and aft of the engine, but in such an installation the need to extract any dropped oil and fuel and regularly clean out the compartment must not be forgotten.

Engine installations carried out on the principles discussed in this chapter will give minimum trouble and maximum safety. Always the emphasis is on safety, and on comfort on board, free from smells and the risks of leaking fuel. It is no foregone conclusion that any yard, or organisation competant to build a boat, will necessarily be equally skilful when it comes to putting in the power unit and a buyer without knowledge of the requirements might well accept work which is not up to standard. One danger, for example, is sometimes found in craft primarily designed as high efficiency sailing boats in which an auxiliary engine is installed on the 'just something to get you home' principle. This type of work sometimes shows skimping on the size or bacing of engine bearers, resulting in excessive vibration and risk of fuel line fractures.

Most engine manufacturers are very willing to advise on installation and if work is being commissioned a safeguard is to insist on the job being done to the recommendations of the Ship and Boat Builders National Federation.

CHAPTER 15

ENGINE SILENCING

Marine engines and their associated components, which includes transmission gear, are producers of noise. However sweetly they run they make combustion and exhaust noise, mechanical noise from tappets, valve gear, timing gears or chains, whines and whirs from gear boxes, dynamos, alternators and belts, rumbles from propeller shafting, hisses from air intakes, clacking and clicking from dogs in certain types of flexible couplings and the more or less unidentifiable sounds associated with vibration. All this goes on inside what is virtually a hollow drum and if life aboard is to be enjoyable something has to be done to control and contain these sounds.

Defence against the clatter is not quite so problematical as might at first appear. The secret lies in absorption. The noises cannot be prevented from occurring and it is impossible to stop or reduce them at source. What can be done is to surround the noise with a substance which will absorb it, or most of it, so that it is totally contained or at least reduced to an acceptable level.

There are many sound-absorbing materials on the market, sometimes in the form of panels which, like building boards, can be sawn, nailed and screwed. Other materials are granular for in-filling, or take the form of plastic foam. Whatever is used should be fire resistant and moisture repellent.

The primary factor in noise reduction is the thickness of the insulating material. While various sound-insulation ratings are claimed (or known, as the result of authentic tests carried out by a reputable authority such as the Building Research Centre), for different materials, the effectiveness of any material in absorbing any specific sound is related to the thickness of the insulating barrier, rather than to its density.

The mechanical noises of engines, gear boxes, and the combustion and exhaust noises are all dealt with by erecting around them sound-absorbing barriers. Engine boxes are lined on all four sides and under the lids. With underfloor installations the floors themselves are lined with, or have built-in, sound-insulation materials. The same treatment is given to bulkheads and to the hull where it is close to the machinery. In larger craft with separate engine rooms or compartments the same methods are used. In whatever way may be possible sound-insulating barriers are erected around the noise source to absorb the sounds and so prevent them reaching the living and working quarters of the vessel.

If properly designed and executed such barriers can be extremely effective as may be revealed by raising an engine cover floor panel of any powerful high-speed offshore craft cruising at, say, 17 or 20 knots, or visiting the engine room of a sizeable yacht with its machinery operating at cruising speeds.

Sound absorption in small boats presents more of a problem because there is often too little space to properly install insulation panelling. But, because the crew are of necessity closer to the machinery, it is equally important to do the best job possible, particularly in power cruisers in which the engine may be running for many hours on end, both by day and at night.

Surrounding working machinery with sound-insulating materials can produce other problems. It is possible that an effective sound absorption installation may prevent sufficient air flow around the engine or its components, in which case serious overheating could occur. Thus ventilation may have to be increased, and if this cannot be arranged naturally, fans and ducting will be necessary.

Only if the sound-insulating material is totally moisture resistant should it be allowed to extend into the bilge. As this is unlikely the installation must go as far down the engine as possible, but stop at a point where it will not be reached by bilge water whatever the motion or attitude of the boat.

Another important point is to ensure that if a granular insulator is used it is all properly contained, so that there is no risk of grains getting free and being sucked into the engine's air inlet. With flexible mountings there must be sufficient clearance between the insulation and the engine to accommodate its maximum range of movement. And again, there must be no interference with the flow of air to the air intake.

There are other sources of noise apart from the actual mechanical and breathing sounds of a running engine. Rumblings and resonances can be set up in other parts of the boat caused by engine vibration, particularly at slow engine speeds. Resilient mountings will overcome this sort of trouble in most cases, but it is important to consult the engine manufacturer before changing over from a rigid installation. If the power unit is flexibly mounted and there is still excessive or unpleasant vibration through the craft and the installation was competently carried out, the problem should be discussed with the engine manufacturer before any alterations are attempted.

The more powerful an engine is the more air it needs and as its power output increases, the faster the air must flow. This inrush of air is not silent and to quieten it down intake silencers, usually combined with air cleaners, are fitted at the engine's air intake. If the hiss is still considered too loud the engine manufacturer may be able to supply or recommend an alternative silencer. However, consultation is necessary to ensure that a different silencer will not upset engine performance.

Apart from actual engine noise, propellers and shaftings are often a source of trouble and it is quite easy to blame the engine or gear box. If the propeller is out of balance, which can relatively easily happen if a blade gets damaged, or if the clearance between the blades and the hull is generally inadequate, or inadequate at certain propeller speeds, or again if there is excessive clearance in the shaft bearings, allowing the shaft to 'rattle', the result can be propeller rumble. This also takes the form of a vibration which can transmit itself to various parts of the hull, or cause interior fittings to vibrate in sympathy.

Broadly speaking the larger the craft the easier it is to isolate the sounds of the machinery, even though the engines are more powerful. There is more space to work in and room to install properly designed sound-insulating systems. There is, too, more physical distance between the machinery and various parts of the ship and those aboard can occupy quarters further away from the sound source. And usually more money is available for linings, furnishings and fittings which all help to absorb sounds and vibrations.

The real problems are found in small boats, particularly when the power unit is a single-cylinder diesel. Often there is barely, or even insufficient, room for the engine under the cockpit floor and sometimes it has to occupy a position in the companion way with its front end hidden under removable steps down into the cabin. In such circumstances sound-proofing is very difficult, if not nearly impossible, but it is worth attempting, by lining any interior surface adjacent to the engine with a suitable sound-absorbing material. It is surprising what can be achieved in the way of increased comfort aboard, especially in a power cruiser where the engine is the only source of propulsion.

Noise and vibration decrease as the number of cylinders increases. The single-cylinder diesel is the worst offender. It has the familiar diesel knock and it thumps. It can become monotonous and somewhat trying after a time except, perhaps, in times of stress, when its continuous audible presence is not unwelcome. The single-cylinder petrol/oil two stroke, on the other hand, is relatively quiet. It has no diesel-like knock and with a big flywheel a lot of the thump is eliminated.

Twin-cylinder units are quieter and vibrate less, petrol or diesel. Threes are better still and fours upwards best of all. Many small four-cylinder engines are remarkably quiet and smooth running. Even so the diesel is usually more noisy than the petrol engine.

Naturally another source of noise, engine exhaust, must be

properly dealt with and effectively silenced. These are matters covered in Chapter 10.

Any effort spent in reducing noise in a boat is worthwhile. Noise induces fatigue which reduces human efficiency. In certain frequencies it can be damaging to the hearing system. It can also lower the ability to hear and distinguish outside sounds and this could lead to danger in navigation.

CHAPTER 16

TYPES OF POWER UNITS

For information on the wide range of marine power units available the reader can hardly do better than refer to the comprehensive data published yearly by the British magazine *Motor Boat & Yachting*. Such information must be treated as 'believed correct at the time of going to Press' for the compilation of such data is a long and involved process requiring a great deal of research, and, because of the time involved, always carrying the risk that some out-dating may occur at the time of, and subsequent to, printing.

To those not previously aware of the number of marine engines available the lists may, at first examination, seem more confusing than helpful. However, systematic study of the data will reveal many similarities, make to make, and it soon becomes quite a simple matter to eliminate units which are clearly unsuitable.

In any case, if they are to be used correctly, such lists should be studied after the basic factors determining the type of power unit have been established. The type of craft, hull form, the use to which it is to be put, whether the engine is to be an auxiliary for a sailing boat or main machinery for a cruiser or working craft, are the sort of considerations which when answered will give some indication of the amount of power required, whether this shall be obtained from a high- or medium-speed engine and what kind of transmission system will be most suitable.

Then there is the choice of fuel, petrol, petrol/paraffin or diesel. Broad categories can be used for guidance:

At present really high-speed engines run on petrol.

Compared with diesel, petrol is more volatile and so more potentially dangerous. It also costs more—very roughly twice as much, depending on the gallonage a diesel craft can purchase at one time.

Petrol engines are generally lighter in weight and less costly than diesels, but their life expectations are less.

Even assuming all fuel lines are properly installed and totally free from leaks or weepage, diesel always seems to smell to some extent, whereas petrol does not.

Petrol accidentally dropped into a bilge will evaporate and may be thus got rid of with adequete ventilation. Diesel oil does not evaporate and can be very difficult to clear from a bilge.

Diesel engines give high torque at relatively low speeds, whereas the petrol engine must operate at high speed to properly develop its power.

The diesel engine is more solidly constructed, weighs more and costs more than the petrol unit, but has long life potential.

Small diesel engines usually run more roughly than small petrol engines, especially single- and twin-cylinder units, which have the characteristic diesel knock rather more prominent than in the multi-cylinder units, especially at low speeds.

The petrol/paraffin engine, while operating on a moderate cost, but relatively inefficient fuel, still requires petrol to be carried on board and involves the additional operating technique of switching over to petrol before shutting down and switching over to paraffin after starting up.

Small petrol/oil two-stroke engines have the advantage of simplicity, lacking valve gear, oil pump and renewable filter, but are prone to oiling up plugs when running slowly and sooner or later involve the user in the difficult problem of cleaning out oily deposits from the exhaust system.

On the larger diesel units there would seem to be little to choose between the four-stroke and two-stroke configuration, choice depending primarily upon which maker's unit specifications best meets the user's needs.

The problems of choice of power unit arise when craft are being designed, or when a sailing boat is to be fitted with auxiliary power for the first time, or when an existing, powered, craft is to undergo a change of engines. So many considerations will affect the final decision and not the least of these will be the user's personal preference in types of craft, fuel and power unit.

CHAPTER 17

ENGINE CONTROLS

Engine operation and boat handling are closely related as functions coming within the general concept of Seamanship, for complete familiarity with the running of the engine, and the effect of the various controls on the movement and handling of the craft, is an essential aspect of safe navigation.

While boat handling is not in itself a subject within the scope of this work, some of the effects must be considered where they are relevant. For example, vessels with a single propeller invariably tend to follow a curved path to port or starboard, rather than run straight, when moving under power. As the engine throttle is opened up this effect becomes more marked and an appreciable amount of helm is needed to correct it and keep the ship on a straight course. The phenomenon is caused by the fact that as the propeller turns the lower blades operate in water of higher density than the upper and the reactive forces thus set up cause the turning moment on the boat. In twin-screw installations propeller rotation is normally arranged to be 'handed' so that, turning in opposite direction to each other, the screws neutralise the effect and the craft runs straight.

Precise control of a single-screw craft by engine throttle and clutch requires quite a degree of skill, whether the hull be of the displacement or planing type, particularly when going astern, which is seldom a very precise business. Many craft do not respond to the helm positively unless a fair amount of speed has been gathered. Twin-screw craft can be handled with more positive control as the operation of one or other throttle will cause a positive turning moment which, while quite effective in displacement craft, can be extremely positive with planing, or semi-planing hulls.

Whatever form the engine controls may take, two criteria must be satisfied. They must be placed conveniently to the helmsman, who himself should be in a position from which he has good all round visibility, and in operation they must be positive giving instant response from the equipment they control, without delayed action or stiffness. If there are two steering positions the duplicated controls must give exactly the same precision of operation. Any engine over 5hp must have a clutch or some positive means of obtaining neutral. On larger power units with single-lever controls there should be some form of positive indication to the helmsman when the control is in neutral. Without such indication it may be impossible for him to be certain whether or not his propellers are stationary.

The recommendations laid down for steering controls are basically the same for speed or throttle controls and may be considered together, even though steering is not itself a function of engine operation.

When the control is by flexible wire or chain pulleys must be used at every point where there is change of direction and the strength of cables or chains, fastenings, bearings and mountings must be adequate for the pulley loads. The positioning of pulleys must be such that there is no risk of the cable fouling the pulley housing and the diameter of the pulley must be at least 10 times the diameter of the cable with a minimum diameter of 2in. Cable tensioners in the form of barrel screws must be placed so that access is possible for adjustment and servicing and they must be wired after adjustment. There should be clearance enough for full travel of the barrel screws.

Where the linkage between control and movable component is by rod or tube compression as well as tension loads must be considered. The strength of such rods or tubes must be adequate to prevent any bending or flexing and long unsupported lengths should not be fitted without guides at appropriate intervals.

All fittings must be protected from corrosion and swivel joints must be lubricated. This means that such components must be positioned so that access is possible, or access must be created. If semi-rigid cables are used the runs should be as straight as possible. Where bends occur the radius should be large. The outer cable must be adequately secured against movement and if the cables are not of the self-lubricating type, greasing or oiling at regular intervals is essential, as laid down by the manufacturer.

In hydraulic systems pipes must be securely installed so that no movement is possible and provision is required for bleeding the system and replenishing the hydraulic fluid.

Gear controls, too, are the subject of recommended practices. In mechanical gear boxes controlled by rods the lever and the linkage must be strong enough to ensure positive action in engagement of the gears and selection of neutral when the clutch is correctly adjusted. The marine gear box is, of course, less involved than the automotive one in that selection is restricted to ahead, neutral and astern, with ship's speed being controlled by the engine revs per the throttle, rather than in combination with the selection of gears of different ratios. Nevertheless, equally positive control is required, particularly when the craft is being manoeuvred in restricted waters. Other requirements are that no load is transmitted by the linkage to the gear lever when engaging the gears, and that the arrangement of the linkage must make it impossible for vibration caused by the working of the craft to alter the setting of the control.

In gear boxes employing a servo mechanism or hydraulic system for gear engagement, there will be only light loadings on the remote control, but the same considerations covering adequate fixing of pipes, bleeding and replenishing the fluid, protection from corrosion and access apply.

While there are a number of sources of supply of control units, most manufacturers follow generally accepted practices in the use of materials such as stainless steel, chromium plated brass and plastics for anti-weathering and resistance to corrosion. Controls should be non-magnetic because they are frequently positioned close to the helmsman's steering compass. Plastics such as nylon and polypropylene are often used for bearings and frames and cable hangers may be of anodised aluminium.

Control units may be single or twin and in either configuration may handle engine throttle only, or throttle and transmission. The design of units must permit easy access to the mechanism for adjustment, replacement of parts and lubrication if necessary. The action should be smooth, but positive and in twin-engine installations the knobs should fall easily under the control of one hand.

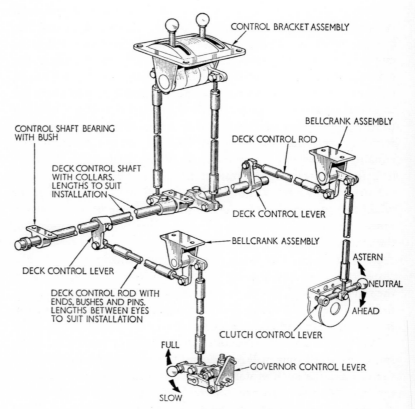

Fig 23   Layout for remote control system

Engine Controls

In larger craft the placing of engine and transmission controls is usually dictated by the layout of the helmsman's console, in which there is a natural grouping of steering wheel, engine data dials, electric switches, fuel switches, navigation instruments and other equipment. In small craft, whether auxiliary sail or power only, it is not always so simple. In sail craft with tiller steering the control is often placed on a cockpit side wall where, perhaps, it is easily handled only when the helmsman is in one position when at the tiller. If he has to stand up, or steer from the opposite side of the cockpit, the control lever may be out of his reach and he may have to change positions to get at it.

In a power craft control may simply be by small lever-operating bowden-type cable for throttle and attached to the side of the engine casing, and gear lever protruding directly from the gear box for transmission. If steering is by tiller this arrangement may not be too bad, but with a wheel located on the cabin bulkhead, as is common practice, considerable movement of the helmsman between the three controls is necessary which, when quick action is needed or in disturbed water, or if a sudden emergency arises, cannot be considered satisfactory.

Whenever possible all the controls should be grouped together in a planned layout at the place the helmsman normally occupies when navigating the craft. If there is doubt about the possibility of using combined throttle and transmission units, control and engine manufacturers should be consulted. Only in the smallest craft can separately acting and positioned engine speed and gear controls be acceptable (Fig 23).

An alternative to the combined single-lever control is the single control unit with separate levers for transmission and throttle. Usually these are of different lengths so that the operator can quickly identify them without having to look at the unit.

Control cables are produced to precision standards giving positive linkage without backlash and are resistant to atmospheric conditions, salt water and unaffected by oil and fuels. Normally of the fixed outer and movable inner type, they are supplied for standard and heavy duties with the necessary fittings. Vernier cables are available where precise adjustment and immediate response are required without being affected by vibration or other factors. Such equipment is normally fitted with some form of quick release allowing normal operation of the cable if required.

Cables with adjustable friction locks are supplied for many purposes in addition to engine and transmission controls. Such locks are adjustable for friction so that throttle settings, for example, can be set against movement of the lever caused by vibration, or for other uses, such as for a choke, or power take off control, locking cables are available without friction devices.

Whatever form engine and transmission controls may take, they must be of such type and so arranged that the helmsman has quick and precise control of his machinery, for in many cases it will be this, rather than his steering gear, which gives him control of the movements of his ship.

CHAPTER 18

FAULTS AND FAILURES

Although marine engines differ in type, size and power output and range from the simple single-cylinder unit to the highly sophisticated turbocharged monster of awe inspiring appearance, insofar as operating principles are concerned they are all basically similar. This means that faults and failures are patternised so that checks, diagnosis and remedial actions may be tabulated. It is now common practice to group such information into quick reference tables, or charts, which can save the operator time in ploughing through engine handbooks and operating manuals.

This is not to suggest that the engine manufacturer's publications should be ignored. Rather should they be read, perhaps studied would be a better word, with care. Not in the sense of a chore, nor as something to be raced through before a new engine is started up for the first time, but, after initial operating instructions have been assimilated, in spare moments perhaps when concentration is possible so that a sound functional knowledge of the particular power unit and its auxiliary components and equipment is acquired.

There is sound reasoning behind these suggestions because although their basic operating functions are similar, individual engines do have their own characteristic quirks and often there are sequences of operations or procedures to be learnt.

As has been mentioned frequently enough throughout this book, the manufacturer's instructions and recommendations should be adhered to. This is not to suggest that the owner must never adapt and devise his own operational habits and methods, but let these be soundly based on the recommendations of the engineers who designed and made the engines and equipment.

Apart from mechanical failure of components due to faulty manufacture, incorrect operation or plain fair wear and tear, most troubles with marine engines and their components probably result from lack of essential maintenance. With the exception of certain types of professional craft which are operated on a controlled schedule maintenance routine and regularly receive attention from trained mechanics, many working boats, and particularly yachts, all too often get little or no attention until something goes wrong. While there may be some justification for lack of attention in the case of the work boat which has to spend long hours daily earning a living for its owner and crew, there can be no excuse for poor maintenance of the mechanics in a yacht.

But, human nature being what it is, it is all too easy at the end of a hard working day or week, or when laying up time comes round, to give the engine merely a quick wipe over, perhaps drain the cooling system and take the mag ashore and leave the rest to weather on with nothing but good intentions to bolster it for the next period of hard duty.

Probably the hard working engine, operating all the year through in all conditions of weather and sea, is better off than the yacht engine which normally has to undergo a lengthy period of inactivity every year during the months when the climatic conditions are the most harmful. Either way the manufacturers provide all the information necessary to maintain their machinery in good order, whether it is operated continuously or not.

What must be remembered is that a marine engine operates in conditions which normally are the least suitable for machinery, in which it is surrounded by and breathes in corrosive elements of remarkably destructive power and which must be continually guarded against. It is also subjected to extremes of temperature and is called upon for many more cold starts in its working life than is the case with the average car, in which the engine often has the advantage of a heated garage to protect it from the worst elements.

Apart from actual faults in starting or running of the machinery, maintenance of the equipment in good working order is mostly appropriate at laying up time or at suitable non-active periods in the operation of a working boat. A systematic sequence of inspection and action saves time and helps to prevent anything being overlooked. A good approach is to start with the propeller, work inboard along the shaft to the gear box, then upwards from the engine sump to the rocker box cover, heat exchanger or header tank, with modifications in procedure of course depending on the type of power unit and its degree of sophistication. Until familiarity is acquired it is wise to have the owner's handbook or maintenance manual in tow.

Small nicks and indentations in the propeller blades can be removed or smoothed out with a file, but more serious damage, such as jagged leading edges, bent or distorted, or badly corroded blades require removal for attention by a professional repairer. It is no good ignoring a damaged, distorted or corroded propeller because it will cause cavitation and seriously lower performance as well as adversely affecting the engine revs and fuel consumption. Vibration, too, is often due to a propeller in poor condition.

The bracket should be examined for security and corrosion and the tail shaft checked for movement in the bearing. These bearings are usually of the Cutlass type which consist of rubber bushes in bronze sleeves. The rubber is grooved to allow water to flow through, which acts as the lubricating medium, and these can become clogged if the craft is frequently operated in sandy or muddy waters. If the tail shaft is worn it may have to be removed for replacement or rebuilding and remachining.

Skin fittings must also be looked at. Water intakes can easily become clogged up with hard packed weed or other substances, or barnacles, which could impede the flow of cooling water.

Inboard, the next for examination is the stuffing box which may need repacking. This means getting out the old packing and fitting pieces of new packing by cutting strips just long enough to meet round the shaft and placing a sufficient number of these with their joints staggered, then tightening down the gland gently enough to compress but not compact them. Further tightening will then be necessary as the new packing is run in.

Cutlass bearings and stuffing boxes are often eliminated in favour of metal or laminated plastic bearings and lubrication may be by grease or water. The maintenance manual will indicate what type is used and detail the necessary attention.

Propeller shaft alignment must be checked from time to time, but not when the boat is out of the water. Any inboard shaft bearings should be dismantled and examined and any grease boxes repacked.

The gear box will probably require no more than a check on oil level and routine oil changes, according to the maker's specifications.

Arriving now at the engine, obviously the beds and bearers should be looked at. Holding-down bolts should be tight, flexible bearers in good condition and bearers firmly secure.

Then the sump should be checked, which leads automatically to querying the need for an oil change. If this has been done regularly, as specified in the book, so much the better. But if not, or if the engine has had many starts with relatively short running time, the oil should be removed and renewed after the usual flushing out. In small craft changing the engine oil can be a chore of the most awkward kind, requiring the flexibility of a trained contortionist, but it is vital to do it before the craft is laid up so that on the subsequent engine run up there is adequate protection against corrosion. With the oil change goes, of course, replacement of the filter element.

Then comes examination of fuel and water pipes, each of which should be in such condition that proper flow of the liquid is obtained. If antifreeze is used it must be checked for proportion, or drained and replaced after the maker's specified period.

All pipe line joints should be examined and pipes inspected for fractures. Any 'dampness' in fuel lines should get particular attention as this may indicate a hairline crack. Filters and bowls must be cleaned and, if the craft is being laid up, fuel tanks emptied. This is sometimes considered unnecessary but condensation will take place during the cold weather and this means water. It is better for this water to collect in filter bowls than in fuel left in tanks. Cooling systems not containing antifreeze must be completely drained for the laying-up period.

On petrol engines, carburettor bowls, filters and jets should be cleaned. The sparking plugs should be removed, cleaned and reset, or renewed, and a small quantity of rust-inhibiting oil injected into each cylinder. A suitable product is RedeX. The engine is then turned over a few times to distribute the oil evenly over the cylinder walls. Old sparking plugs may then be used for sealing the plug holes. (Before the engine is started the following season it should be turned over a number of times with the plugs removed in order to expel any surplus inhibiting oil which might otherwise foul up the running sparking plugs and make starting difficult.)

The procedure is much the same for diesel engines. Inhibiting oil is used in the cylinders and old injectors used for sealing up. The operative injectors should be cleaned and stored dry or replaced as necessary.

All the electrical installation and circuitry must be carefully looked at. Damp air, particularly when it is salt, plays havoc with electrical connections and components, producing the green corrosion which if left will build up resistance in joints and allow faults and failures to develop. All exposed parts, and this applies to those under cover, but not in permanently heated, dry compartments, should be protected against corrosion, by greasing or by the use of a proprietary inhibiting product such as will be found in the range available from the Plus Gas Co Ltd of Acton, London W3. Any corroded parts must be stripped down, cleaned and then protected. Periodic examination of the electrical installation, which includes of course batteries and their installation, terminals and connectors, is particularly important in craft which operate all the year round and are subject to extremes of climatic and sea conditions.

Only the broad principles of machinery maintenance and laying-up procedures can be given here. For specific detail the manufacturers' handbooks must be used. It must be admitted, however, that not all makers' publications are sufficiently comprehensive or clearly written. Such publications are sometimes produced by engineers who, while experts in their own field, are not well versed in the arts of conveying information in a meaningful way to those without engineering or mechanical knowledge and ability. Sometimes the trouble lies in the use of engineering terms, or part names, which mean nothing to the layman and so should be explained in words that he can understand. Fortunately, there has been considerable improvement in the writing and presentation of handbooks and service documents during recent years and this is very welcome because the danger is that the ordinary boat user may not, rather naturally, take the trouble to seek interpretation of a mass of technical jargon, or badly worded or presented material, and so proceed in ignorance until some trouble or failure occurs. If this happens at sea or in difficult conditions, clearly worded, easily understood manufacturer's information is essential.

If faced with this type of communications problem the best solution is to have a word with the Service manager, preferably in person, or by telephone. Writing a letter is not very satisfactory because it will often bring a reply of similar form to that which has presented the problem in the first place.

There are, of course, many qualified and competent marine engineers and firms available for service and repairs. In seeking their assistance it is advisable to try to find out if they have agencies for, or knowledge of, the particular engine or components involved. While any qualified marine mechanical, electrical or service engineer should be competent enough to deal in principle with any aspect of marine mechanical and electrical equipment and installations, those who specialise in particular makes get to know their peculiarities and can often take short cuts to solving problems, thus saving time and money.

So much for general outlines on maintenance. What about fault diagnosis? Because, as already mentioned, marine engines and much of their ancillary equipment are, in the engineering sense, similar in characteristics and function, it is possible to tabulate fault diagnosis under broad function-failure headings and to give leads which, unless there is mechanical failure requiring extensive dismantling and renewal, will enable the boat user to take remedial action, or at least locate the failure and report intelligently to the service engineer.

Most fault diagnosis tables, however, tend, for perfectly good reasons, to give only the barest of clues, checks or actions and there would seem to be scope for rather more detailed explanations of certain items. The information which follows applies equally to petrol and diesel engines unless otherwise stated.

ENGINE STARTING

Starter motor does not turn
The starter motor pinion may be locked on the gear ring. Free off by turning shaft with spanner applied to squared shaft end.

The starter motor may have failed or the switch or solenoid may not be operating. Consult a service engineer.

The battery may be low in charge or discharged, or defective. A clue to battery low in charge could be chattering of the solenoid. The battery terminals or cables may be loose or corroded.

For some reason it may not be possible to turn the engine. It might be seized. Or have water in the cylinders. This could happen due to broken cylinder head gasket or cracked water jacket, or as a result of submersion. Remove plugs or injectors and turn engine to investigate.

Faults and Failures

Starter motor turns but engine does not

The starter motor pinion may not be engaging with the gear ring due to trouble or dirt in the Bendix drive or because the starter is incorrectly positioned.

Starter motor turns the engine over too slowly to start it

Low charge battery.

Defective battery. Loose or corroded battery connections. Faulty starter. Wrong grade (viscosity) of engine oil, too thick at low temperature. Get engine started by hand cranking or with spare batteries, run up to working temperature, drain engine oil, flush out, refill sump with correct oil or with multigrade. It may also be necessary to renew the oil filter.

Poor compression is a cause of difficulty or failure in starting. This may be due to: Loose cylinder head; damaged cylinder head gasket; worn cylinders; worn pistons; damaged, worn or gummed up piston rings; worn, broken or burnt valves or stems or valve springs causing: bad valve seating; insufficient lift from seatings; valves sticking in guides. The fuel supply may be faulty because: the fuel pump is not operating efficiently, or not at all. Check for punctured diaphragm, dirt, or broken spring preventing valve functioning. If the pump has to lift fuel more than about 4ft it may not be of sufficient capacity. Or the lift may be increased beyond the pump's capacity when the boat is heeled or rolling. This would cause intermittent running. Insufficient baffles in the fuel tank allowing too much surging could cause fuel pump starvation when the craft is rolling and pitching. Or there could be restriction in fuel lines due to choked filters or pipes of too small internal diameter.

In diesel engines the fault could be due to worn injection pump element or delivery valve, or the element is failing to

222

operate. The atomiser may be faulty, the injection pump
rack not operating or the hot bulb failing.

If the fuel pump sucks air check the system for fractured
pipes, insecure pipe joints, faulty filter gaskets, sufficient
fuel in tank. If pump is operating but fuel does not flow,
check system for blockage in line or filters, carburettor
jets, fuel cock not turned on.

Examine choke for correct operation.

In petrol engines the ignition may be faulty because: the
coil may be defective. Check for spark at coil HT to earth.
If there is no spark examine the HT wire for breaks and
make sure it is not too loosely fitted. Check that contact
breaker points are opening correctly and clean, test the
condenser, check the LT circuit for faulty ignition switch
or wiring, check battery charge, clean or tighten battery
terminals.

The magneto may be at fault due to defective armature or
magnet failure. Check contact breaker as for coil ignition.

If the coil gives a satisfactory spark there must be an
interruption in current flow somewhere between the coil
and the sparking plugs. Check these first. They may be
oiled up (particularly in two-stroke engines), wet with fuel
through over choking, wet with water through damaged
cylinder head gasket or broken water jacket, or the porcelain
may be cracked or dirty.

If the plugs are in order check the plug leads for damaged
insulation, connections to plugs and distributor cover,
breakage of the wire. Excessive moisture or dirt on the
leads can prevent current reaching the plugs. If the plug
leads are in order examine the distributor. See that the

cover is not dirty or cracked which could cause current tracking. If in doubt renew the cover. Check that the spring-loaded brush is free to make contact with the rotor. Check that the rotor is not cracked or earthing.

If the magneto gives a satisfactory spark carry out the same checks of leads, distributor, plugs as for coil ignition. If these are in order check that the timing is correct.

Engine runs but operation is intermittent and unsatisfactory
Most of the faults which can cause spasmodic running have already been described. The cause will be either unsatisfactory fuel supply and/or ignition or mechanical defects. Points to check are: fuel in tank, full flow fuel supply, no air in diesel fuel, no air locks in petrol lines, no water in fuel, no dirt in carburettor, no flooding in carburettor, correct amount of air mixing with fuel. Check compression.

A poor or badly installed exhaust system can cause poor running. It should not have more bends than absolutely necessary and the internal diameter of the pipes must not be too small and there must be no restriction to gas flow. Two-stroke engine exhaust systems are prone to clogging up with oily waste and they are very difficult to clean. After many running hours it may be better to replace pipes and silencers rather than attempt to clean them. Four-stroke systems seldom clog up in this way. In a 'wet' system poor engine running could result from moisture being drawn back into the cylinders.

In petrol engines intermittent interruption of ignition current supply could be caused by spray affecting the HT leads and causing shorting, or the same thing can happen if the leads are too long, or not adequately secured, so that with the motion of the boat they foul something and the current shorts to earth.

If a governor is fitted it should be checked. Incorrect assembly, non-functioning springs and loss of vacuum can cause intermittent running.

Engine runs but is lacking in power
It is inevitable when considering factors affecting the running of an engine that repetition occurs, because different symptoms can, and often do, have the same causes. For example, an engine which starts but will only run intermittently may do so for the same reason as another which runs but does not give proper power, eg fuel starvation, so that under the various faults will be found the same check points repeated. Thus, if the lack of power is due to insufficient fuel getting to the cylinders the cause may be—no fuel in the tank or failure to switch in the reserve tank; carburettor jets partially blocked or butterfly not opening properly in a petrol engine; pump rack failing to allow full fuel flow in a diesel; in a petrol engine the inlet manifold may be leaking air, thus weakening the fuel mixture, the check then being for tightness of all manifold nuts or if necessary withdrawal of the manifold for examination of the manifold gasket. Lack of power may be caused by a general de-tuning of the engine after a considerable number of hours running and perhaps a lack of regular maintenance. In a petrol engine ignition timing and valve clearances, sparking plugs, HT leads and coil should be checked. In a diesel the injection timing may be out. In either type of engine the compression may be down.

As has been covered in detail in Chapter 2, to operate properly within its performance specification an engine must receive an adequate supply of fuel in the correct proportion of diesel oil or petrol, and air. Restriction in the supply of air, therefore, can be a cuase of power loss. This may be due to a dirty air filter or one choked with an overdose of oil, or it may be difficult for the engine to get an adequate supply of air because it has to operate in a badly ventilated, over-heated engine room. Or a choked exhaust system can have the same effect, causing high back pressure.

Lack of power can be due to outside factors such as fouled propeller (a frequent occurrence in weed-infested waters particularly noticeable in small craft as a sudden change in engine beat and loss of way). It can usually be cleared by putting the propeller in reverse for a few seconds, then going ahead. Or the sterngear bearings may tend to 'pick up' through lack of greasing or lubrication, a condition which if allowed to continue will quickly result in seizure. A bent propeller shaft will put undue loadings on the engine, as will, for example, an incorrect reduction gear.

Observation of exhaust smoke
The colour of the exhaust smoke can provide many clues to the condition of an engine and it should be periodically observed, not necessarily only because engine performance is below standard or suspect. The observation must only be made when the engine has reached its normal operating temperature. If at this condition the exhaust shows appreciable blue smoke it means that lubrication oil is being burnt and the reason for it should be sought. It may be nothing more serious than too much oil in an oil-bath-type air cleaner, or the amount may be correct but the oil is, in effect, being 'spilled' over the correct level due to violent motion of the boat, or if the cleaner is of the wire-wool-type it may have been over oiled. Any of these factors will allow oil to be drawn into the induction manifold which will cause the smoking. If, on the other

hand, the blue smoke is caused by the lubricating oil getting past the pistons, matters are more serious, being due to mechanical faults or failures such as worn, broken or incorrectly fitted oil scraper rings, worn pistons, or wrongly designed pistons, the lack of skirt scraper rings, distortion of the connecting rod, badly worn or scored cylinders or worn valve guides. Not so serious, but still producing the same symptoms, would be an incorrect engine installation angle or even operation of the craft in badly trimmed condition. Blue exhaust smoke at normal operating temperature, if due to mechanical defects, may not indicate an essential need for an immediate strip down. If the amount of smoke is moderate and the engine runs smoothly without excessive or unaccustomed mechanical noises, there may be many hours of reliable running before overhaul becomes necessary. On the other hand, if there is a lot of blue smoke and oil consumption is high an engineer should be consulted because there must then be risk of mechanical failure sooner or later.

Black smoke in the exhaust at normal operating temperatures indicates fuel faults. It is due to poor combustion resulting from inadequate vaporisation or atomisation of the fuel which can be due to incorrect operation of injectors or the injection pump in diesels or misuse or faulty mechanical action of the choke in petrol engines.

Engine runs hot
When an engine persistently overheats under normal operating conditions this is an indication of malfunction and investigation is necessary. Localised overheating, such as when running for a period at full power or prolonged idling coupled with inadequate ventilation, is to be expected and need not cause concern if the circumstances are under control. But the gauges should be watched for any indication of excessive temperature rise.

Overheating can occur through a persistently weak fuel mixture, incorrect ignition timing or spark too far retarded in a petrol engine, a malfunctioning cooling system or mechanical defects in the engine or ancillary engine-driven equipment.

Cooling systems can become choked up with scale, pumps may not operate efficiently due to loose or broken drive belts or because of impeller damage. The thermostat may be faulty, there may not be enough water in the system, hoses may collapse, keel coolers and heat exchangers can become blocked or partially obstructed, cylinder heads may leak due to faulty gasket, an air lock can occur and impede water flow, the sea cock strainer may be choked or the cock may be only partially turned on.

In an air-cooled system trouble will occur if there is any obstruction to the full flow of cooling air. Assuming the installation is correct and adequate in the first instance, the cause could be a blockage in the entry or exit trunkage or ducting, malfunctioning of a fan or insufficient ventilation of the area from which the cooling air is drawn.

If the overheating is of a mechanical nature it could be caused by insufficient lubrication due to the oil level being too low, or not being circulated properly when the craft is heeled over for long periods as when tacking, or because the engine angle of installation is incorrect. Alternatively the means of cooling the lubricating oil may be inadequate, there being insufficient air flow over the sump or oil cooler.

On the mechanical side tight bearings may cause over heating, as will any component parts which, moving in contact with others, are running out of true to the extent that excessive friction is set up. Over tight drive belts can also cause trouble by overheating themselves and putting unnecessary loadings on generator and water pump bearings.

Other signs of overheating are running on when switched off and pinking under load.

Engines normally run reasonably hot and need to for best efficiency. The operating temperatures specified by the manufacturers should be adhered to as nearly as possible. Temporary overheating is not dangerous, but it is best that the operator should know the reason for it.

CHAPTER 19

ENGINES OF THE FUTURE

Looking into the future is at the best a speculative exercise, full of pitfalls for the prophet whose concern is with any sphere of technological development. However, in the realm of marine power units of the type covered in this book there is perhaps rather more limited uncertainty about what changes may take place within the next four or five years, or even the next decade.

The reason is, of course, that marine engines, for the smaller craft not classified as ships, originate as automotive units, mostly of the industrial type and their transfiguration into marine units depends upon the work of marinisers who may or may not be the manufacturers. This is a good idea, for if marine engines had to be specially made as such, few makes would be available and then only at prohibitive cost.

The boat user therefore has to rely upon the automotive engine, the product of quantity production, for his power unit and on the skill of the marine engineer for its adaptation to meet his needs.

That this arrangement has now been brought to a fine pitch of practice is all too evident. The majority of pleasure craft are fitted with engines of one sort or another and seldom does one hear of working craft being out of commission through engine breakdown.

There are, of course, manufacturers producing marine engines as such, but in the majority of small craft today it is the basic automotive unit which sits on their engine bearers. It is thus to the automotive industry that we must look to get any clues as to possible future developments. First, though, one may ask why is it necessary, if today's marine engine has been brought to the present state of development where it is reliable, economical and hard working, to look for yet further advancement or even different types of power unit altogether?

The answer, surely, is contained within the question. The present state of achievement could not have been reached if designers and engineers were not continually seeking to improve, develop and progress their brainchilds. While 'if it is going, leave it alone' is without doubt sound advice for the boat user, it will not do for the development engineer, whose whole life is dedicated to improvement. To achieve better performance, lower fuel consumption, increase reliability, obtain smoother, quieter running and match engineering skills to new designs are his constant aims.

In the marine field, as in the automotive world, racing plays a big part in development, forcing under the task master of competition, new ways and means, fresh approaches, new materials from the designer's board.

An example of this is the Ford Turbo Plus, brought to an extremely high pitch of performance from what was basically a tractor engine, because of the call from racing men for ever more power. The new design was produced and after the engineers had achieved the desired power output, one hundred engines were made, bespoke for racing drivers who were to test for a factor even more essential than sheer performance—reliability. At the end of a hard racing season the engines had proved themselves and they are now available to designers and users of high-speed cruising craft, giving more power and better performance with no weight penalty. This development was no exercise undertaken for profit. The creation of the new engine and the initial batch of one hundred was a charge on development and no light one at that. Subsequent orders for Turbo Plus units for racing and cruising craft are at best a drop in the ocean in relation to Ford's daily output of engines. And it must be remembered that when the units leave the Ford works they are not marinised.

Nevertheless, the design work was done and the engines were produced because development engineers must always go on and because an organisation like Ford have the resources for them to do so, and who is he that will scorn or denigrate this probing forward? May it not be that the owner of a Ford-engined (or for that matter any other engined craft, for technological progress is seldom restricted to one mark for long) vessel or car will benefit from that little bit more reliability, economy or power output?

Probably the most realistic probe into the future would be conducted along two main channels. Further development of the established marine engine and the design and development of entirely new configurations of machinery such as the rotary engine. There may perhaps also be further research into other forms of fuel, such as steam and paraffin. Although in practice the steam engine has virtually disappeared, designers' interest has never completely waned. Now, the Chrysler Corporation and the Steam Engine Systems Corporation are jointly involved in an American project to develop a steam-powered passenger car. A British engineering company, Ricardo and Co Ltd of Sussex, is to be responsible for detailed design of the reciprocating expander and the US Government is sufficiently interested to award certain contracts in connection with the project. If the development results in a satisfactory steam car engine suitable for quantity production there would clearly be potential in the marine field.

Paraffin as a fuel does not seem to lend itself to serious development interest, although there are a number of industrial power units available which could be adapted for marine use. But paraffin is a relatively dirty fuel. It forms sulphur and carbon more readily which means engine overhaul must be more frequent and then there is always the problems of dual fuel systems because of the necessity to start up on petrol. Comparatively speaking power, too, is reduced with paraffin because of its lower calorific value which necessitates lower compression ratios.

Developments most likely to take place within the next few

years will almost certainly relate to the use of diesel oil as a fuel. Up until fairly recently high-speed power units were invariably petrol engines, but now diesel engine speeds are rising and, because also petrol has become increasingly unpopular as a fuel to have aboard a boat, it may well be that, except for certain types of racing craft, the diesel engine will become the universal power unit of the next decade.

On the design side, already considerable progress has been made to meet the demands for compactness, better power to weight ratios and improved power to bulk ratios. Matters such as fuel injection ratios, pressures, hydraulic volumes, timing, smoothing of inlet and exhaust ports, swirl rates and combustion chamber shapes have had designers' serious attention with demonstrable performance improvement. Piston speeds, too, have been considerably increased. At one time automotive diesel engines were governed at 1,800rev/min. Now speeds of 2,200rev/min are common in this sphere and the potential is better still for marine diesels which, because they have unlimited supplies of cooling water and operate in only narrow load and temperature ranges, can be boosted to, and allowed to operate at, far higher power outputs than would be possible with vehicle installations.

Another approach to greater power output being used by some European manufacturers is the attainment of higher rev/min without increase of piston speed by using short stroke V6, V8, V10 and V12 engines. As an example of this technique, the Cummins V8 which gives 240hp from 9·1l at 3,300rev/min, which is about the same power output as in-line engines nearly twice the size, are producing at around 2,200rev/min.

Foden and General Motors are meeting the demand for more power from less bulk with the development of two-stroke diesels which have now reached a high standard of reliability and which, at power outputs in excess of 200hp, begin to level out their inherent higher costs.

There is yet another factor playing a highly significant part in the present and future development of the diesel automotive engine and which will undoubtedly be of significance in marine applications. It is, of course, the effect anti-pollution and anti-noise regulations, now coming into force throughout the world, will have on the design and operation of internal combustion engines. Whatever may be the technological involvements one thing can be taken as a certainty—a rise in unit cost, which, in the long run, will be borne by the engine user.

However, the diesel engine has a fundamental advantage as far as pollution goes. It is less of a polluter than the petrol engine because, although both push out carbon monoxide, carbon dioxide, hydrocarbons, nitrogen oxides, sulphur dioxide and carbon or soot, the diesel produces only minimal quantity of the poisonous, invisible carbon monoxide. This is because the diesel operates with a large proportion of air which means that the proportion of carbon monoxide in the exhaust is low and thus easy to control. It is also low in output of hydrocarbons which with nitrogen oxides largely contribute to the formation of smog.

When it comes to nitrogen oxide the diesel engine is no better than the petrol engine and so far as smoke and noise are concerned it can be a lot worse.

British diesel engine manufacturers have already gone a long way to making their units comply with the regulations which have been known for some time and thus the effect, in unit cost and in other ways, may not be all that burdensome for the marine user. It is, however, of some significance that designers are seriously exploring the development of alternative types of power units. British Leyland are among those manufacturers carrying out comprehensive trials of gas-turbine-powered trucks and in Germany a city bus has been running on liquefied natural gas which is claimed to reduce pollutant emission by between 60 and 80 per cent.

So much for developments related to fuels. What of power units themselves?

For the reasons already given it seems very unlikely that an entirely new type of marine engine will emerge in quantity production over the next decade. The development and small quantity production costs would seem to rule this out and so again we have to look to the automotive industry.

Here, the most likely development is the realm of the rotary engine, the most advanced of these being the Waniel which, after many setbacks, is now in quantity production for automotive use in Japan and under active development in many other countries. In fact one company in Sweden, Marin Wankel of Stockholm, is marketing a unit known as NSU Marine Wankel Ro 120F, which is claimed to give 120hp SAE (107hp DIN) at 6,000rev/min. There is also a larger unit, the Ro 135B, giving 135hp SAE (115hp DIN) at the same speed. Operation is on diesel fuel and the units are offered with Z-Drive type Zahradfabrik-Friedrichshafen Z14.

The Wankel engine was invented by Dr Wankel, a German, and it forms the basis for most rotary engines, being extensively patented. In principle the rotary engine offers appreciable advantages over the reciprocating power unit. It has no parts which move up and down and so does not have to withstand the intense loadings to which, for example, pistons are subjected. It is lighter in weight, more compact in configuration and has less moving parts than the piston engine. It is also relatively free from vibration and much quieter running.

The basic unit consists of a fixed casing with an internal shape approximating a wide-waisted figure of eight, and a rotor of roughly triangular shape. Multiples of rotors may be used, phased together, for more power.

In action the rotor revolves eccentrically within the casing with the three triangular tips in constant contact with the internal surface. Connection of the rotor to the output shaft is through planetary gearing. The output shaft is equivalent to the piston engine's crankshaft.

Combustion chamber spaces are recessed into the rotor flanks and these link as they revolve with carefully designed internal faces of the casing in such a way as to give expansion and contraction of their size. The casing is provided with a fuel inlet port, one or more spark plugs and an exhaust outlet port.

The cycle of operating is the same as in the piston engine, namely induction, compression, power and exhaust, but because there are three chambers, one in each flange of the triangular rotor, there are three power strokes per one rotor revolution. Normal carburation or fuel injection may be used and cooling may be by water or air. For successful operation highly effective seals must be maintained between the three tips of the rotor and internal faces of the casing.

Another non-reciprocating engine development is being undertaken by the Central Research Department Experimental Station of the E. I. du Pont de Nemours & Company (DU PONT) at Wilmington, Delaware, USA, under the direction of Dr W. A. Doerner.

This is known as the Du Pont Rankine cycle engine and a 20hp version has been used for the laboratory experiments.

The engine uses external combustion to heat a fluid held in an annular chamber by centrifugal force. The vapour from the fluid drives an internal turbine which rotates at 27,500rev/min and operates a drive shaft. After driving the turbine the vapour condenses and is channelled back to the ring-shaped boiler. The unit is normally air cooled, but could be water cooled for marine use.

Two advantages of this particular development in the principle of the turbine power unit are the absence of an external blower to force air over the condenser and the elimination of a separate pump for returning the condensed fluid to the boiler. These factors reduce internal power consumption and simplify design.

It is not the intention of the Du Pont Organisation to build and market these engines, but to seek suitably qualified licensees throughout the world.

Yet another approach to the development of an engine without reciprocating parts is being conducted by a UK company, Rotor Power of Chester. This is a rotary piston unit in which all moving parts rotate about their centres at a constant angular velocity. The design principles are claimed to allow a wide range of configurations and in addition to normal fuels an adaptation for steam could be designed.

MAJOR ENGINE COMPONENTS AND MATERIALS

CYLINDER BLOCK: Usually takes the form of a monobloc, that is, the block and upper half of the crankcase forming a single casting in iron or aluminium alloy.

CYLINDER BORES: Bores must be smooth and very hard wearing. Machined in the block they have a ground, honed or hard chromium electro-plated finish, or they can be inserted sleeves or liners which may be replaced when worn. Liners are essential in aluminium alloy blocks.

CYLINDER HEAD: Cylinder heads are machined from cast iron or aluminium alloy. They are a critical factor in engine design, containing the valves and combustion chambers and inlet and exhaust ports. Today some cylinder heads are flat, the combustion area being formed by a recess in the pistons.

PISTONS: Pistons used to be made of cast iron, but now the material is usually aluminium alloy which is lighter and conducts heat away quicker, although expansion is much greater with heat. For this reason a fair amount of clearance is allowed between the pistons and cylinder walls leaving the piston rings to maintain compression. But too much clearance causes piston slap when the engine is cold so special techniques are used to control expansion such as cutting slots in the lower portion of the piston, known as the split skirt, and using low expansion materials for struts. Probably the ideal piston material has yet to be found.

PISTON RINGS: Made from high grade, high resilient cast iron. Each ring has a diagonally cut slot allowing it to be sprung open slightly for fitting to the piston and to allow for some movement in operation. If, after a period of service, an engine shows some loss of compression and higher oil consumption, it is sometimes possible to give it a further spell of useful life by fitting new rings. But because cylinder bores wear oval there is a limit to the amount rings can take up. It may be less expensive in the long term to rebore and fit oversize pistons and rings, or put in new liners with standard pistons. Manufacturers usually recommend standard overhaul procedures.

GUDGEON PINS: Often hollow to save weight, the gudgeon pin forms a pivot for the piston in the little end of the connecting rod. It transmits piston thrust to the rod and is made from a high tensile steel forging or specially tough forged aluminium alloy known as Duralumin or Hiduminium.

CONNECTING RODS: High tensile steel forgings are used for connecting rods which have to withstand considerable stresses in transferring the vertical motion of the piston into rotary motion of the crank. The top, known as the little end, clamps on the gudgeon pin. The big end is split to allow assembly on to the crankpin and machined to take bearing shells. Assembly is by high tensile steel bolts.

BEARINGS: Little end, big end and main bearings are usually made from a special alloy known as 'white metal' which, although relatively soft, is highly resistant to wear and has low friction and low melting point. Should there be a lubrication failure these bearings will 'wipe', or partially fuse, before total seizure can take place. The metal is bonded into semicircular bronze or steel shells made in standard sizes which drop into position in the bearing housings and require no internal machining or laborious hand fitting.

CRANKSHAFT: The main reciprocating component of the engine. Carrying the webs and crankpins, flywheel and timing gear drive, it transmits power to the propeller or gear box. It is forged from high tensile steel or a specially strong grade of cast iron which is cheaper, but can be used with the larger bearing surfaces of today's designs.

CAMSHAFT: Camshafts used to be machined from solid steel, but current practice is to use special cast iron with the cams in correct position, ready for machining to size.

CAMS: Eccentric projections on a rotating shaft which lift cam followers such as, in a marine engine, tappets or rockers, or the movable arm of the contact breaker.

TAPPETS: The cam followers in the valve-operating mechanism.

In a push-rod engine they locate the rods which then connect with the rocker arms. In an overhead camshaft unit the tappets act directly on the rocker arms.

VALVES: Operating in the cylinder head the inlet and exhaust valves have to withstand very high temperatures and constant hammering against their seats. The stems must stay true and the heads resist burning or pitting. Exhaust valves must be particularly resistant. Very high quality steel containing tungsten and other elements is used.

ANCILLARY COMPONENTS: Many other parts are used in the final build up of an engine. Nuts, bolts, studs, bushes, ball races, oil seals, valve springs and essential items such as carburettors, fuel pumps, dynamos or alternators, starter motors, fuel injectors, sparking plugs, distributors, all are necessary to make up the complete unit. Many items such as carburettors, fuel pumps, distributors and other ignition equipment are of proprietary manufacture, to be found on many different makes of engine.

ACKNOWLEDGEMENTS

I wish to thank all the firms, organisations and individuals who have provided information and given me assistance in compiling this book. I am sure they will appreciate that the range of products and services covered is too extensive to permit individual mention, but because of the very detailed advice and help provided by The Ship and Boat Builders National Federation and the Marine Division of CAV/Lucas, upon which I have been able to build the structure of recommended practices, it is only right that these two organisations should be named.

INDEX

Index